GARY

GARY

Brian Masters

JONATHAN CAPE
LONDON

For
Juan Melian

First published 1990
© Brian Masters 1990
Jonathan Cape Ltd, 20 Vauxhall Bridge Road, London SW1V 2SA

Brian Masters has asserted his right
to be identified as the author of this work

A CIP catalogue record for this book
is available from the British Library

ISBN 0–224–02727–1

Phototypeset by Computape (Pickering) Ltd, North Yorkshire
Printed in Great Britain by
Mackays of Chatham PLC, Chatham, Kent

ONE

WHEN I FIRST saw him he was sitting on a wall of the estate, smoking a cigarette and beating the bricks with his heels. Gary looked idle and bored. There was even, dare I say it at this distance, an air of stark cynicism about him, as of one who did not see the cars and people passing by him because they did not matter, could not interrupt his solitude and would not help if they did. It did not surprise me that I was arrested by the sight of this weary child, then aged thirteen. Far more surprising was the indifference of everyone else, the blank blindness of strollers and shoppers who brushed the space of a potent forlorn image and appeared not to notice. Gary had all the beguiling attraction of youth, the soft indefinite features, the unlined innocence and gentle demeanour, but they were overlain by a harshness that was worryingly anarchic. The radiance of youth had been supplanted by the sullen shiftiness of the misanthrope. I felt depressed as I walked on.

I quickly forgot, however. There was little room in my life for rumination on the whimsical jumble of fates which assign misfortune to some and abundance to others. Squeezing twenty-five hours from a twenty-four hour day was the sum and scope of my problems, for I always appeared to have too much to do, yet was restless if a spare hour threatened me with its emptiness. A dedicated list-maker, I bounced through the day with a succession of ticks as one task after another fell to my relentless, even slightly deranged, need to accomplish. I usually had a book on simmer, as months of research, organisation, distillation spawned yet more lists, then a chapter was launched and six days of exhausting concentration would be lavished upon it until it, too, could be ticked. There were book reviews once every three weeks or so. And I tucked in an hour or two when necessary to prepare for the American summer-schools which I helped to organise at Oxford every year. They were − still are − a refreshing invigorating break from the agony of constantly building and fashioning sentences.

I had a house in West London which I shared with several others − on a more or less permanent basis − though I was in every real sense living alone. At one point there were five of us, three men and two women, pirouetting round each other but never colliding. They were all good friends, although I had not been 'attached' to any one of them. I had never married. I did most of the cleaning myself (not as a therapy − I disliked it deeply − but because I could do it better than anyone else and it added to the ticks I could chalk up for the day), some of the shopping, and looked forward to an evening at my club as a reward for the day's efforts, where one could talk freely and widely about anything except home. Yes, there was a lot to do. There was no room for any more tasks.

It was, therefore, with no small irritation that I responded to a call from Norman Galway. Norman was due to take a group of my American students to some of the art galleries in London two days later. He had to opt out, he said, as his wife was going into hospital for a check-up that day. He couldn't let me down at such a late stage, I told him, I would never be able to find a substitute, and was not up to taking the tour myself. He said he could do it another day. No, the coach was booked and the galleries alerted. Couldn't he see his wife later, when the tour was finished? Well, there was more to it than that, he said. His wife's grandson was at home, and he had to be looked after. Norman would have to stay in simply to watch over the boy. Well, if that's all that's troubling you, I said, send him over to me! I'll look after him for one day and give him some lunch. That was 'very kind' of me (it wasn't – I was desperate he should do the job). Would I care to pop over tomorrow to meet the boy, and Mrs Galway? We agreed that I should have a snack with them in a hamburger bar (easier to locate on the street map than their flat), in case I wanted to withdraw my offer.

Thus it was that I sat opposite Gary at McDonald's and immediately realised this was the same listless boy I had spotted on the wall a few weeks earlier. With him was an ample, jolly woman in her sixties, eating heartily if somewhat messily, pausing occasionally to plop a wet kiss on the boy's temple, which he did not resist. I could not help noticing that Gary kept putting bits of his food on the woman's paper plate. It soon became apparent that whatever he rejected – a tomato skin or the top half of a dry bun – he passed over to her rather than shift to the side of his own plate. She made no objection; it was obviously a routine performance. His discomfort at having unwanted things in front of him was removed by her willingness to accept them. He was not to suffer irritation; she would absorb and neutralise it.

Mrs Galway initiated the conversation. Wasn't the weather dreadful? All this heat, she couldn't stand it. It didn't suit her. She was only saying to her Norman the other day, that was her hubby, a dear man, she'd do anything for him, she was saying that it was the bombs which interfered with the climate, and he agreed. After all, it wasn't natural, was it? Then,

'My Norman's so good with Gary here. See, Gary's home from school tomorrow, upset tummy he's got and it wouldn't do to play about with that, would it? I mean, he's got to take

7

care of himself, I'll see to that. Trouble is, I'm under the doctor myself at the moment and he's *so* busy, I can't afford to lose my appointment tomorrow, so my Norman's had to cancel his day's work so he can stay at home with Gary. Not a murmur, not a whimper. He's so good.'

'What are you under the doctor for?' I asked.

'Glands,' she said. 'It's glands what makes me so fat, and the doctor has just the right pills for them.' I wondered why an appointment was necessary in order to collect pills, but said nothing.

'He's a very good guide, you know, one of the best, he is. So thorough and knowledgeable, that's why they're always giving him work. You'll have a devil of a job replacing him at short notice. But he's never short of work. They're all very loyal, the tour companies, they know when they've got the best, know what I mean?'

It was then that Gary eyed me with a glance I can only call conspiratorial. I decided to bring him into the conversation, to find out what he was thinking.

'Have you been on guided tours of London with your grandfather?' I asked him, adding rather patronisingly, 'I bet that's fun.'

'Yeah,' he said. 'I know London like the back of me 'and, could take you anywhere, I could. Been with Norman all over the place. But he's not my grandfather. Nobody is.'

The large woman felt obliged to interject. 'I'm his nan,' she said, 'but I married my Norman much later, after he was born. I'm all Gary's got, really.'

That 'really' must surely conceal mountains, I thought. I was sufficiently intrigued to risk an intrusion. 'What about his parents?' I asked.

'Gary's mum was my only daughter, Grace, beautiful girl she was. Everyone said so, she was a real darling. Going to be a model, she was, you wouldn't look at anyone else once you'd seen her. Great big brown eyes and shiny black hair, there was no one to touch her. She died young, poor girl. Only twenty-two. We don't like to talk about it.'

Gary, who had in the meantime shoved some chips on to his grandmother's plate and was drawing deeply on a cigarette, said nothing in the warm silence that followed, but contemplated the table, then looked over to me again, challengingly it seemed, as if he expected me to contradict.

I said, 'I'm sorry to hear that.' Then, if only to break the unnerving pause which again followed, I gave the news which Norman had obviously not revealed. 'Look,' I said, 'there's no need for your husband to miss work tomorrow, Mrs Galway . . . '

'You can call me Dopey. It's really Polly, but Gary always calls me Dopey, and the name's stuck. He will have his little ways.'

These were not the little ways I then felt disposed to adopt. 'Mrs Galway . . . Polly,' I stuttered. 'I've already spoken to Norman, and we've agreed. Gary's coming over to me for part of the day. I don't live far away, just off Ladbroke Grove, and I can deliver him to you when you get back from your doctor's appointment at the hospital.'

'I know you're local,' said Polly. 'I've seen you around before. Well, if you really don't mind . . . but we shouldn't trouble you.'

I was about to declare that there was no trouble at all, when Gary took charge.

'Can I, Nan? Oh *great*! I'll be good, I promise, honest I will.' For the first time, his face came alive, eyes agleam with the anticipation of adventure, eyebrows raised, a broad smile conquering inert features. Not waiting for Grandmother's assent, which I could hardly doubt would be forthcoming, as he manifestly knew all too well, he thumped the table with both fists.

'You won't be able to smoke in my house, mind,' I said, wishing to establish authority from the start, without quite

9

knowing why, and noticing that he appeared to welcome the interdiction. I wrote in ball-point pen on a paper napkin, 'Brian Masters, 4 Temple Grove Road, W11'. Polly gave her grandson another peck on the cheek before they got up. Over her shoulder as she left, she called out, 'You won't have to give him nothing to eat. He gets plenty at home. I see to that.'

Gary's first visit to the house was marked by a litter of clues strewn from his fingers and his lips, clues whose significance I was not yet ready to appreciate. I am not sure, now, that I would have acted differently even had I been prescient enough to see what those tiny indications forebode. Hindsight carries too much baggage of analysis, of sifting seeds from the sand, and buries the pure, uncontaminated feeling of the moment beneath its bright mound of reasons. I did not have the freedom, anyway, to act differently. We are prisoners of our responses, which we cannot control, deny, or dissemble. Gary knew how to pump those responses. He had a cunning and a wisdom which, viewed in retrospect, were terrifying. Then, however, they were manifest only in inchoate charm and a wild, soaring need.

He arrived punctually, so punctually that I suspect he had walked around the block in order to ring the bell at exactly the correct time. Luckily, there was no one in the house that day, so he was able to prowl and territorialise without hindrance. He wanted to look into every room, touch every wall, open every cupboard door, which I permitted because the rush of his enthusiasm banished any thought of prohibition. He was curious about objects and things, whom they belonged to and why they were there. His interest in people was minimal, except in so far as they were also 'possessed' by someone. He was anxious to discover who surrounded me, owned me, had claims upon me, as if weighing whether or not I was an object worth picking up and examining.

10

I told him that I shared the house with friends, an actor and actress, who stayed as sporadic lodgers whenever their work in the provinces released them; and an elderly lady with a colourful past. More than that he did not need to know and, indeed, was not disposed to find out. His only urgent question was whether I had children. I told him frankly that I had not, and that I had so far resisted marriage. Gary was visibly pleased with that.

'My dad lives in Birmingham,' he volunteered.

This rather took me aback. It was the first time a father had been mentioned. Polly Galway had only spoken about Gary's mother − her daughter − and I had thoughtlessly assumed the father was unknown. 'What does he do?' I asked.

'Dunno. Drives a lorry or something. Anyway, I don't care. He never did anything for me.'

'Don't you see him very much?'

'You must be joking. Only seen him once in me life, and he kept having a go at me. He can't stand me, rotten sod!'

'Having a go', an expression I was to encounter frequently in subsequent months, meant naked hostility in Gary's view of the world. He was not about to tell me more, and his bravado was obviously spurious. He *did* care, and I determined to find out how there could exist such division between father and son. But that could wait. He asked if he could visit again, and wanted to write down the telephone number but experienced great difficulty in forming the numbers.

'What school do you go to?' I asked.

'St Jude's, over by Maida Vale. But I don't like it much.'

'What don't you like?'

'They're always having a go at me, won't leave me alone. So I don't go much. Let 'em stew.'

It transpired that Gary had been such a repetitive truant that he had barely been at school more than three days a year. His grandmother was aware of this and encouraged him to persist in his truancy, on the grounds that it was bad to make a child do what he did not feel like doing, and anyway education wasn't everything and she was able to provide for all his needs. Gary could hardly read or write. He had been robbed, by indulgence, of his right to compete and shine with his peers. Grandmother had sought to protect him, and had instead deprived him of identity. He was little more than the map on which she had written her love. The selfishness of her attentions must have produced in him a chaos of greed and inadequacy the contemplation of which stirred parallel anger in me. When he should have been at school, he had wandered by the sides of canals and meandered in public libraries, fingering the books whose delights were forbidden him.

Lying on my desk was an unopened parcel. Gary asked if he could open it for me, a task he performed with the impatience and relish of someone about to lay claim to a new possession. His world was scattered with unopened parcels, each of which might contain the magic ingredient to make his life rich and rewarding. He tore off the string and cardboard with such eagerness that he also ripped the dust-cover of the book inside. I was alarmed at this display of indiscipline (and not a little peeved that the book should be wantonly damaged) and scolded Gary severely. Afterwards, 'I think it's about time you left,' I said. 'I'll drive you home.'

The effect of this incident upon his humour was quite unexpected. It ought, I imagined, to have provoked anger or resentment, or at the least another show of brave unconcern at the opinions of others. Instead, he left the study in downcast fashion and, having allowed him some moments to reflect, I went to find him. Gary sat on the edge of the bed in the guest room, his face white with dejection, the same forlorn, empty gaze I had first seen when he sat on the brick wall. He said nothing. He did not weep, though it was not fanciful to see the substitute for tears churning in his stomach. My show of displeasure had devastated him, because he did not know what had caused it, did not understand that his actions could excite reproach. He had never been reprimanded.

I placed my hand on his shoulder. 'It doesn't matter as much as all that,' I said. 'Cheer up!'

For a long time he remained silent. At last, 'You mean I can come again?' he said.

'I should think so.'

Some time after Gary had left, I noticed that the whisky bottle was missing from the drinks table. I felt reasonably sure I had not discarded it empty, and could only surmise that the boy had done something with it. Not, of course, drunk it; he was certainly no incipient alcoholic, an affliction he could not have concealed. But what had he done, and why? I did not find it for weeks, and then only by accident. Gary had placed it carefully out of sight, behind some books on the shelf, and forgotten about it. There would have been no point in asking him to remember – the bottle had ceased to exist the moment he had banished it from view, which is what he intended it should do.

It was a bottle of Teacher's.

Something else. Upstairs, where he had repaired to dwell upon his destruction of my parcel, I found his jumper. Did he leave it there by accident, or by design?

The following day Gary telephoned. He was chatty, even ebullient, and asked when he could come to see me again. I said I would take him to the cinema one evening soon, but first I wanted to talk to his grandmother. I arranged to see her on the afternoon of our projected excursion.

The flat where Polly Galway lived with her husband and grandson was on the top floor of a modern rectangular block at the confluence of two main roads. Such blocks have become depressingly familiar of late, and this one bore all the usual signs of neglect by the authorities and contempt by the

13

inhabitants: walls vivid with graffiti, landings spattered with broken bottles, lifts stinking of urine and only fitfully in operation. Gary hovered at street level waiting for me. I suggested he go out and leave me to talk alone with his nan. They were both reluctant, he because he did not wish to be left out of any conference which concerned him, she because she did not want (or dare?) to disconcert him, but they finally agreed on my undertaking to tell him afterwards what was said. It was quite clear, anyway, that she would keep nothing from him.

Polly lounged full-length on the sofa, this being the position which could accommodate her great girth. Her husband sat on a chair at the round kitchen table struggling with a crossword puzzle. Having thanked me for enabling him to fulfil his engagement with the tourists, he then said no more. He appeared not to be listening. This is what Polly told me:

'Gary was born on the same day that James Dean died, that's how I remember, because we all thought wouldn't it be lovely if he was reincarnated or something. Silly, I know, but there you are. He was such a bright little boy, from the word go, wouldn't let his mother out of his sight, he wouldn't, always let you know when he missed her. He would bawl his eyes out until she came back. He knew what he wanted, that one. He worshipped his mum, would have licked the ground she walked on given half the chance, but the poor little blighter didn't understand that she had her own life to lead. Well, how could he? So he came to me for his dinner, and I washed his things. Grace said to me, you can give him the love, Mother, and I'll look after the discipline. I suppose she had to make him toe the line a bit, he was so demanding, but I always made up for it when he came here every day. Trouble was, my Grace was her own worst enemy, really. It was such a strain, the training for her modelling career, you know, that she took to the bottle, whisky, that is. Not so much as you'd notice, don't get the wrong idea, but she needed a tipple

14

when she got home, and I couldn't stop her, could I, because I didn't know how much the strain was telling. I mean, it wasn't me who was trying to get a career going. Another thing, she never knew how to handle men. They took advantage of her and she just let herself in for more of it. Gary's dad was typical. I was living in Portsmouth then, taking in lodgers, paying guests who'd have their breakfast and evening meal cooked for them, and very good it was too. My Grace was only fifteen. This young man comes looking for a room, takes the room and gets my daughter into the bargain. Then as soon as Gary's born he pisses off, pardon my language. Never was any good, that one, a real tearaway, looking after himself with not a thought for anyone else. We never saw him from that day to this, and good riddance. Gary never set eyes on him until last year, and that was a mistake if you ask me. So Grace and me, we brought the boy up together. Like I said, she looked after the discipline, I looked after the love. Pity she had to die. She just tried to take too much on herself, that's my opinion.'

Rather different versions of this history were to be revealed as time went by. For the moment, Polly's account was all I was vouchsafed. She seemed to me a monstrously stupid woman. As if reading my thoughts, Mr Galway lifted his head from the newspaper to address his own few words to me.

'Polly is a very special human being,' he said.

Polly blushed girlishly.

The evening at the cinema was startling. It began simply enough, with the common requests which turn a mere film into a treat (Can I have some crisps? Can I have some pop?), and to which I naturally acceded. We settled in the front row of the circle, because Gary wanted to spread himself, and would have put his feet on the seat-back of the row in front, which might not have been convenient for anyone sitting

15

there. As we were, the only impediment he might cause would be to his own view of the screen.

The film was *Rollerball*, an American confection which I confess I did not understand, in which two rival teams of hefty men hurtled at high speed round a racing-track on roller-skates. The object appeared not to be to reach a destination first, but to inflict the most damage on the opposing team. Bodies slammed into walls, faces crushed against floors and boots, fists rammed into eyes and blood spurted copiously. Of course, there was nothing specifically to 'understand' – the film-makers knew that perfectly well. The film was designed to reach a depth of yearning in the audience for violent display, to set the pulses racing and stir some kind of dark libido. With Gary, they succeeded all too well.

From being fidgety and nervous, he grew more energetic with each bloody encounter, jabbing the air with his forearm, bouncing in his seat, applauding, even gurgling slightly, and finally standing up to yell at the screen. I had physically to quell his enthusiasm, to hold his wrist down beneath my grip, and threaten to take him home. For a moment, the excitement subsided, but not for long. Again, the juices would come rising, and Gary was on his feet, turning with glee upon the people behind who remonstrated with him, to shout and pour scorn upon them. The ritual preparation for a fight was being enacted beside me, its forces stronger than any control I could summon; primitive impulses were in danger of smothering the inhibiting factor which makes the lives of most of us tolerable and decent. Gary had no inhibiting factor. He was about to be unleashed, and he welcomed it.

Two young men came down towards us in a threatening manner. Ignoring me, they pointed fingers at Gary and told him, sneering, to keep still.

'Just you try and make me!' said Gary, and before the contest could be engaged in earnest I had grabbed Gary, protesting, by the arm, and dragged him out of the cinema.

He felt the humiliation keenly, and yet part of him, I could feel, was unburdened by authority curtailing his flood of passion. 'What d'you do that for?' – hurt, resentful, un-comprehending – was soon replaced by, 'Good job you were there, Brian, or I don't know what I would've done' – half boastful, half relieved, and not a little frightened.

Gary was not introspective, he did not understand the springs of his own nature, nor would it have occurred to him to look for them. Power, force, the brutal expression of potential, were clearly of paramount importance to him, and the fact that he lacked that inhibiting factor was at once a source of pride and of nightmare. He must have noticed that other people were more in control and, though he would not wonder why he was not so, he would wish that he were. A lot to deduce from one visit to the cinema, perhaps, but I have never forgotten the impact of that evening, nor what it presaged for the future. I felt then that this boy was in distress, that it had nothing to do with me, and that his problems required the attention of professionals. I had stumbled into his confused life for no reason and with no plan. I did not belong there and would extricate myself as soon as decently possible. He may have been reading my thoughts in his canny, vigilant, alert way. 'Everybody dies on me,' he said. 'Don't you die too.'

Far from extricating myself, I grew steadily more involved. Gary's visits became frequent, and I found myself absurdly flattered that this child should want to spend so much time with me. Every time he contrived to forget something when he left, a box of matches (I now allowed him to smoke – first round to Gary), a jacket, some old photographs, until there accumulated a motley collection of his things piled up in the guest room. We spent much of the time watching television, or rustling up meals, in a curiously domestic way. My own life continued, with lectures in Oxford, lunches out, dinners at the club once or twice a week, but I now found myself considering Gary's movements as well as my own, and tailoring my engagements to avoid disappointing him. The fact that the school summer holidays were still in progress meant he could turn up at any time of the day (I determined that he would return to school in September, but I had not thought it through, neither how I was to make him nor whether it was my position to intrude at all). He gradually became more proprietorial. He was, little by little, *adopting* me.

The day came, of course, when he finally staked his claim.

'Can I stay the night?' he asked, out of the blue. When I did not reply immediately, he added, to reassure me, 'Go on, Nan says it's all right. I've asked her. She says you'd be a good influence on me. I can have that room at the top, can't I. I'll keep it clean and tidy, promise, and I won't make any noise.'

'That's not the point,' I said, stubbornly. 'You don't live here, and you mustn't get used to the idea that you can come and go as you please. When school starts, you'll have to get back to normal, and I won't let you come and visit except at weekends.'

'Fuck school,' he muttered, almost talking into his armpit.

'Listen, Gary,' I said, trying not to sound self-righteous, 'school is your only chance. If you don't learn to put up with doing things you don't want to do, you'll never get anywhere, you won't know what you can do and what you can't do because you won't give yourself the chance to find out.'

'Well, I'll try. OK?'

'We'll see about it,' I floundered, my defences scattered. 'Tell your nan you'll be staying here for two days at the weekend, if you like. But only on one condition.'

Gary leapt from the chair, actually laughing. 'Great!' he said. 'I'll bring extra clothes, and my school books, so's you can have a look.'

'You've forgotten something. I said there was a condition.'

'What's that, then?'

'I want you to bring me the address of your father.'

'What d'you want *him* for?' He spoke with a mixture of contempt, disbelief, wariness.

'I want to talk to him.'

'That'll spoil everything, that will, you wait and see,' he continued. 'I might as well give up now.'

'Why should it?'

'He'll tell you a pack of lies about me, and you'll believe him, that's why.'

'Trust me,' I said, and regretted it immediately. Trust is not something one can command, least of all from a boy such as Gary. 'I'll make my own mind up. But I mean it. I won't have you staying here unless I can talk to him first.'

'He knows nothing about me,' he shouted defiantly. 'And he doesn't want to. You'll be wasting your time.' Gary was worried, anxious lest his character be betrayed by prejudicial gossip. But I thought I also detected a different apprehension; he would have liked to show pride in his father and their relationship, however distant, and he did not want me to discover (although he had told me himself) that there was no cause for any such pride. He did not want me to see his wounds.

It took some courage on his part to relent. 'OK,' he said, 'Have it your way. But don't say I didn't warn you.' His desire to wave a wand of change was so strong that he was prepared to risk having it broken like a dry twig in his hand.

Mr Callinan (strange that I had not known Gary's surname until then) was polite and surprisingly confidential on the telephone. He told me that he had married Grace when she became pregnant and moved with her into a flat near her mother's. When I said that nobody had told me about a marriage, he was not taken aback. 'They wouldn't tell you,' he said. 'They want to give the impression that I was the villain of the piece, but it wasn't like that at all.' Grace had been so totally dependent upon her mother, Polly, that the marriage had been a farce from the start. Polly smothered her daughter, cooked for her, washed her clothes, did her shopping, so that Grace had no need to move by her own volition. She spent all her time with Polly, and he, Callinan, was a mere appendage at the other flat, reduced to eating in cafés and knocking on his mother-in-law's door (for he was not given a key). 'She also bought all Grace's drink for her, and she'll do the same for Gary if he doesn't get away, you mark my words. Mind you, he probably won't want to get away, she will have seen to that.' When Gary was born, he was taken to his grandmother's and dumped. Grace never changed a nappy, bought any clothes, or raised a spoon to his mouth. Callinan was not welcome when he went to see his son, and eventually found the door permanently closed. 'They wouldn't even answer any more when I knocked. The two of them stole him and kept me away from him. They seemed to think all men were suspect and interfering. I threatened to intrude upon their cosseted little world, and they were bent on keeping me at bay. I think the mother found it unbearably sordid that her precious girl had even been touched by me.' After a few months, Callinan left for good and sued for divorce. Some years later he married again, and settled in Birmingham, where he had two stepchildren, sired by his wife's former husband, but none of his own. He had seen his son Gary only once since then. The boy had written to him asking to see him, and had taken the train to Birmingham, where he stayed just five days in the marital home. 'He was impossible, causing such disruption in my house that I had to thump him every day, several times a day. He quarrelled with my wife and with the kids, put broken glass in their shoes, threw his dinner at the wall and refused to clear it up, was always fighting with someone. It was dreadful, you wouldn't believe it. I packed him off back to London, I had to. He caused mayhem. He'll never come here again, and I doubt if I'll ever see him. Polly's responsible for him. However he turns out, she'll bear the blame.'

Callinan had no idea what life had been like for Gary after he had left, whether Grace had found another man or not, though he doubted it. He had only learnt of her death by official letter; the mother-in-law had not seen fit to inform him, not wanting to have him sully the funeral with his presence or intrude upon *her* private grief.

He wanted to know if Gary ever mentioned him. 'Rarely,' I said, 'though you are never far from his mind. He would like to get on well with you.'

'Then why did he cause such havoc when he was here?'

'Can't you see? You have two children who are not yours by blood and to whom you give all the paternal affection which he thinks is his due. They live with you, are welcomed home by you, take breakfast with you, and he rumbles around in his solitary world miles away from the one person to whom he properly belongs. You don't have to look further than plain jealousy. Frankly, I don't blame him.'

There was a pause before Callinan replied. I anticipated hostility, rancour, even threats. After all, this was *his* business, not mine, and I was, to him, no better than an interfering stranger with unknown motives and a patronising manner. He would have been quite right to give me a few home truths and hang up. But he didn't.

He began to cry.

It was only a gentle weeping, but I heard it none the less; it stumbled into his mouth and cluttered his words. 'I hadn't really thought of that,' he said. 'You could be right. I've always wanted to know him, but somehow everything was against me, and then it got too late. When he finally did come here, and was so bloody, I thought there was no hope at all. My wife could kill him, she could. She won't ever have him in

21

the house again, won't even hear his name, that's how bad it is.'

'I'm sorry,' I said.

'Yeah, well, there's nothing we can do about it now.'

'Yes, there is.'

'What do you suggest?'

'I think you ought to see him down here in London. You drive a lorry, you must come this way from time to time. Take an hour off to spend with your son. It would mean so much to him. It could actually help him move forward, and you might well enjoy seeing him alone, in circumstances which do not press against him so strongly.'

'My wife must never hear a word about it,' said Callinan.

'She won't from me, and she can't from anyone else.'

We made a plan without setting a date. He would meet me at a motorway café somewhere out of London, so that we could chat for a while and prepare the ground. I welcomed the idea, because it would give me an opportunity to present myself, as it were, not for his approval but for his information, and then withdraw. I would take him to my house and go out, leaving him and Gary together. Neither of us mentioned the need for secrecy from Polly Galway – that was taken for granted. She would do everything in her power to prevent such a meeting. I also decided that I would not tell Gary until the date was secure; to awaken his fears and enmity, his anxiety and his spleen, the rich kaleidoscope of confusing undermining emotions that his absent father evoked, and then to let them fester and collide and erupt inside him for days on end, would be wickedly cruel. Meanwhile, I had to wait for Callinan to be in touch, and I found myself hoping he would, with that same painful uncertainty that I imagined would besiege Gary. This was what the psychiatrists doubtless termed 'identification'. Its insinuating tentacles were beginning to alarm me.

*

Gary brought enough clothes to last him not two days, but a month. Of course, it was an adventure for him, a game to be relished, but there was something more earnest than that. He was taking possession. His behaviour throughout the weekend was angelic. He peeled the potatoes, scrubbed the kitchen floor, took the rubbish to the bin, swept the garden and looked for weeds. He even went out of his way to ingratiate himself with the neighbours, offering to run errands for them to the local shops, whose location he lost no time in discovering. He made himself pleasant, useful, above all *known*, introducing himself to the butcher and the green-grocer as if enlisting their alliance in what was clearly destined to be a major campaign. He offered sage, solicitous advice, like that of an experienced man of the world addressing a clumsy-footed tyro ('You ought to do something about that tap in the bathroom, Brian. Reckon it needs a new washer. I'll see to it for yer'). The most outrageous, and endearing, demonstration of this frenetic usefulness came when he quite unnecessarily took the wheel off my car and replaced it with the spare ('That tyre was getting a bit bald. You'll be all right now'). I confess I was impressed that a boy of thirteen could undertake such a task, let alone accomplish it with aplomb; I would have been quite incapable. Gary wanted to make himself instantly indispensable, irreplaceable, and he set about his purpose with dire determination. It was a thoroughly enjoyable weekend, and he a thoroughly delight-ful companion.

There were tiny signs which caused me some appre-hension, though Gary was not to blame for them so much as his grandmother. She had given him far too much pocket money, £30 I think it was, and I was fairly sure that her motives were not to save me expense but to remind him that her indulgence was unlikely to be matched. She also made it known that she was not feeling very well. Polly was forever feeling unwell, and not all of her ailments could be attributed

23

to chronic obesity. Gary was visibly affected when Nan was ill, fretting about her and wondering aloud if she would be all right. It required no great percipience to spot the root of his worry; that he might lose someone else to the whims of mortality made a momentary cloud pass behind his eyes. I thought it reprehensible of Polly Galway to purchase her grandson's attention with gold and with fear. Had she been malign, it would have been even worse. But at that stage I was convinced she had no idea what she was doing. Gary telephoned her three times a day to enquire after her health.

On both Saturday and Sunday night he asked me to go to his room and tuck him in. It was already, by the way, 'his' room rather than the guest room. Gary's use of the possessive adjective was generous, to say the least. No sooner did he have something than he surrounded it, subsumed it, swallowed it, until it had no existence unrelated to himself. He spoke of *his* bed, *his* cupboard, even *his* car, within seconds of having seized them. It was an acquisitiveness derived not from greed, but from desperation. His happiness seemed to depend upon rights of tenure.

When he left on Monday morning, going home alone, it was without sadness, for he clearly did not regard his sojourn at Temple Grove Road as an interlude. I knew that I could no longer deny him access to my home without crucial damage to his well-being. The dangers and responsibilities of the situation were not far to seek, yet I had no time to dwell upon them or banish them with careful forethought. The boy's arrival was like the advent of a storm which refused to subside; there was no sheltering from it, no turning it aside. I was very rapidly being kidnapped, and I felt unable to resist.

On the desk in my study I found a curious piece of paper on which had been drawn, in pencil, two heads, below which was a rough scrawl meant to represent water. The figure on the right was identified in writing, 'This is Brian', that on the left, 'This is Gary'. Most curious of all, the 'Brian' figure was in

24

difficulties – he appeared to be drowning. From his mouth issued a balloon of speech, which said, 'Save me, Gary'. The Gary figure also spoke; it said, 'Hold on'.

I stared at the scrap of paper for nearly an hour, bewildered and oddly touched.

TWO

THE SCHOOL WHERE Gary was nominally a pupil remembered him well, but not with kindness. I went to see the headmaster a week or two before term started, and heard another recital of disruption and decay. Gary rarely bothered to turn up, and when he did he was just as likely to walk out of class after a few minutes, shouting obscenities and slamming doors. He had made some little progress just before he went to Birmingham and even produced some written work, but afterwards went into reverse. He was a thoroughly bad influence upon other children. The head, Mr Macpherson, a balding, round-faced, but still youngish man whose weary eyes betokened the pressure of his calling, admitted honestly that he thought little could be done and, what was more, had little heart to do it. There were other boys and girls who deserved more the time and attention of his staff, and who were more likely to respond.

Macpherson was naturally curious to learn the grounds for my interest in 'the case' and I told him briefly how Gary was busy inveigling his way into my life and that I thought, having allowed this to happen, I owed him some attempt to assist in the reconstruction of his hopes.

'You may regret a deeper involvement,' he said. 'The boy is profoundly disturbed, and anyone who comes close to him, who tries to relieve his turmoil, will feel the sparks. The only way he can measure his effect upon people is to demand too much of them, and when they can't deliver, to make them smart.'

'That sounds rather melodramatic, if I may say so.'

'Believe me, Mr Masters, there is no room for melodrama in my job, and no need to invent it. These kids are all learning in their various lights how to make waves – much more interesting than logarithms and irregular verbs, you will agree – and young Gary makes his in a particularly unsubtle fashion. He is essentially destructive. We had a teacher here once who was so frightened of his power, not physical, you understand, but power to undermine confidence, to emasculate with iron defiance, that he had to take a week's leave. Of course, we have a duty to try, even with boys like Gary, but it can be a dispiriting experience. And, of course, distressing. In my profession, an admission of defeat is the first step towards atrophy of the soul. We are here to help young people mature. If we can't do it, we question our purpose and our vocation. A teacher cannot bear to recognise his uselessness.'

'And you think any guidance offered to Gary Callinan is destined to be useless.'

'I'm afraid so. It has to be. He needs to make people face their uselessness in order to confirm his own despair and pessimism. He must prove to himself that he is right to expect nothing from the world. Like the Devil who tempts, he secretly wants his victims to resist, but when they do not it hardens his own security.'

I was not happy with the diabolic metaphor, with its suggestion of determinism and innate evil, but had to acknowledge that Macpherson spoke with the heaviness of experience.

'I still think it is worth a try,' I said. 'One can't abandon the boy to his demons.' (The word was intrusive and involuntary, an echo of that wretched metaphor.)

27

'I do hope you are clear about your own motives, Mr Masters. You will feel virtuous in making an effort, but you must remember that your virtue is not of value. If you fail, Gary will be just as abandoned as before, if not more so, and your self-esteem will be of no earthly use to him.'

'You are very frank,' I said, somewhat stung.

'Well now.' Macpherson smiled, leaned forward behind his desk, clasped his hands and abruptly changed mood. 'How can we help?'

I told Macpherson that I would personally guarantee Gary's attendance at school, and would take responsibility for his behaviour there, if he would in turn bend the rules to allow Gary two afternoons off each week. There was a practical aim in this as well as a wily one. Somehow or other, I would engage a private tutor to do remedial work with Gary, improve his spelling and reading, so that, in time, his presence in the classroom would not be wasted. It would be no good for him to compete and find himself bottom of the class at every turn – there must be for him some prospect of pride. The other benefit I envisaged was that he should know he was receiving some kind of special treatment, and that he would rise to it. The danger was, of course, that he would interpret special treatment as yet more indulgence, and that I would compound the damage inflicted by his complacent grandmother, but it was a risk worth taking, for he had to earn the indulgence by attendance at school the rest of the week; it would not be given *gratis*.

The headmaster agreed. He gave me a list of private tutors used to remedial work, with a letter of recommendation from himself. We shook hands and he wished me luck. I knew he meant it.

The following day I went to see Mrs Galway and Gary and told them of my plan. Gary was predictably excited. 'A private tutor!' he exclaimed. 'Wow! Why can't I have a private tutor all the time?'

Was this what Macpherson meant? Demanding too much in the knowledge it would be refused? Inviting disappointment? I preferred to think it was more likely to be genuine apprehension; he was afraid of lining himself up against others at school, and who could blame him?

Polly Galway made no objection. On the contrary, she was so fully in favour that I would not have been surprised had she and her grandson discussed the matter in advance of my arrival, or rather that he had made his intentions clear and she had endorsed them, obliging as ever. What none of us had mentioned were the implications for Gary's domestic life. There was not the slightest chance that Polly would insist upon his going to school, even with my promise to the headmaster in the background; she would join him in dissemblance if necessary. Nor would I want the individual lessons twice a week to take place in the *laissez-faire* ambience of her disordered household. I knew what would have to happen. So did Gary.

'Reckon I'll have to come and live with you,' he said, half-heartedly, unsure of this part of the bargain.

'School starts in two weeks, so you'd better move in as soon as you like.'

The boy's features exploded into a broad grin. He jumped up and punched the wall forcefully with his fist, opened the sitting-room door and closed it again, swung it to and fro between both hands. He could hardly be contained.

He disappeared into another room and began throwing things out of the wardrobe, piling them on the bed and on the floor, muttering to himself. Polly could only grin and simper, sinking her chin into her ample breasts. 'What a lad,' she said, 'what a lad.'

*

I had made a point of exchanging some cautionary words with Polly while Gary was out of earshot. I knew that The Plan could so easily be thrown into disarray, demolished, by grandmother's lenity or connivance, and yet I had no moral right to tell her how to behave. I was very much the interloper, a sort of *deus ex machina* about to inject a new dimension into her world, and however outwardly compliant she was, I need more than her complacency in order to promote Gary's resurrection: I needed her active alliance. At the same time, there must be no suggestion that she was about to surrender her grandson to a stranger who had arrogated authority over him. It must be a shared endeavour, which she must welcome, without being made to feel that her own shortcomings had made it necessary.

'Polly,' I said, 'if this is going to work, we have to deny Gary a lot of the privileges he has taken for granted, for his own sake.'

'What privileges? We're nothing special. We've never had privileges, as you call them.'

'I mean the privilege of coming to you for whatever he wants, the privilege of having you wash up after him, the privilege of having you make excuses for him.'

'Well, that's normal, isn't it? I've always done my best for him, as any mother would. I've treated him like my own son.' She was not defensive, just surprised.

'I think, honestly, a mother would have scolded him from time to time.'

'Oh, he's only a boy,' she said. 'He's no worse than any other little boy who gets up to his tricks.'

'He's not so little,' I said, 'and if he continues to behave like a little boy who can do no wrong, he will come up against people who do not forgive him everything as you do and he won't know how to deal with it. He won't have the resources.'

'So I've done the wrong thing in washing up for him, have I? Well I never!' Polly giggled and looked purposefully coy. To her the idea was absurd. It even appeared rather crass to me when put with such clarity.

'Not quite,' I answered. 'But I shall ask him to wash up after meals, and I shall expect him to do it. He must realise he will lose something by refusing. He will gain nothing but aimless power.'

'Well, all I can say is that I wouldn't give tuppence for your kitchen if you let him loose in it. He'll make a fine old mess.'

'That's as may be,' I said. 'He'll learn. And there's another matter which is even more important.' She looked at me blankly, though I detected a flicker of apprehension behind the eyes. This was not going at all well. Polly was beginning to feel she was under interrogation. 'Gary has got to realise,' I continued, 'that a constant flow of money does not represent salvation. Now don't protest, Polly. I know you've been wonderful to him, and you've always given him as much as you could from the housekeeping budget, you would rather go without yourself than stint him. You are a very generous woman. But you must see that he will never be able to recognise the value of economy, or make ends meet, unless he has to measure one advantage against another and choose which he prefers. At the moment he gets the impression that all want is solved by the supply of loot. It is a remorselessly commercial view of desire and satisfaction, and it does him no good whatever.'

'But you have to give him pocket money,' she insisted. 'He's got to have something to buy an ice-cream with. And he'll have to have his fare to go to school.'

'Yes, of course. I intend to get him a school pass for the buses, which will upset him for a start, because he will expect to be driven by car every day. As for the rest, I'll give him regular pocket money, about two pounds a week, which is more than he will need unless he wants to buy packets of cigarettes and cans of beer every day, and he must make it last. When it runs out, he *must* realise that there is no more until the next instalment. I know it sounds harsh, but I promise you every other child has to learn to live with it.'

'How do you know? You haven't got any kids.'

'A lot of my friends have, and I've watched them. Most of them are much better off than Gary, with far less.'

'I don't get it,' she said. 'You talk in riddles. Anyhow, if you're the one who's doing it, why are you telling me?'

'Because I'd like you to resist the temptation to supplement his income, to give him more when he comes here in search of it. He might get angry, but he'll do you proud in the end.'

'A little treat now and then never did anyone any harm. I'll tell you that for nothing. That's what grannies are for. There are some things I know more about than you.'

'Yes, Polly, you do. I'm not sure that I know what I'm doing. But I want to try. Will you help me?'

She shrugged her shoulders. 'Let's have a cup of tea,' she said, 'you'll feel better.' It was as if she pitied me for some curious defect of personality. I noticed that she did not give me her agreement, nor did she argue further. The subject was closed. I realised then that she was afraid of her grandson, and that she was capable of lying not just to protect him, but to absolve herself.

The next week was spent in frantic activity. Gary and I went to a clothing store to buy his school uniform and some shirts. Also, to his disgust, a couple of ties. To make him feel that his new territory was not transient, I had a house-key cut for him and placed on a key-ring which bore his initials. This was not enough. He painted GARY'S ROOM on the door of what had been the guest room, and asked if he could have some brand new sheets for the bed. I opened a small bank account in his name, hoping he would save something from his pocket money and add to the balance, thus enjoying the fruits of economy. It might also, I thought, help him to regard himself as 'grown-up', no longer dependent upon gifts. He relished all this as a mark of status, but as yet he was unable to see it as anything more than the kind of indulgence he had been used to. I was, I now know, idiotically naïve, expecting him to recognise that he had to deserve bounty. Such an upheaval in moral perception could not be achieved in a few days. I was naïve in a different way, too. I did not pause to consider how much I was enjoying these outings myself, what novel pleasure I derived from the sensation of instant parenthood, taking on the exquisite exhilarating enchantment of responsibility for a young life without having worked for it. That I was giving myself some satisfaction was, I suppose, entirely wrong, for my own needs were not important, or so I thought. I was busily convincing myself that my impulses were altruistic, and this was a kind of wilful self-deception. For how could I embark on such a programme unless it gave me some benefit as well? If any good was to come of this it would have to be an exchange. But I was far from wondering what I hoped to win for myself.

There was one encouraging sign in that last week before term. Gary quite properly wanted to go out in the evenings and make himself known to other boys in Temple Grove Road. He wanted to show off, to stamp his identity on the neighbourhood, seek out his tribe and establish his place within it. Much sniffing and jostling for position would be part of the exploration, and I was happy to support it. The whole process of 'belonging' demanded that he find his niche and fight to maintain it. That he spent his time hanging around on street corners with groups of other boys did not matter; better that than watching television alone.

Gary asked me what time he had to be in and ready for bed. I said eleven o'clock. Virtually every night that week he came through the door at five past eleven, not so late as to incur displeasure, but late enough to invite notice. Often he was puffing and panting, having rushed to be home in time, and pushed out a quick 'Sorry!' as he clambered upstairs to his room. I looked at my watch and pursed my lips. This was evidently what he wanted. Had he been early, he would not have elicited any reaction from me. Had he been reprehensibly late, he might have risked rebuke. By being just late enough, he registered that there was somebody, at last, to whom it mattered what time he came home.

Gary grew increasingly nervous as the day approached when he would have to bare himself for public examination at school, expose his talents to scrutiny and risk the revelation of their meagre quality. He was not afraid of being put to the test – in fact he welcomed the exercise in private and repeatedly sought my help in spelling and expression. One of his most urgent desires after moving into Temple Grove Road, for example, was to write a letter to his grandmother. It was the first he had ever penned, and he wrote it out three times, painstakingly, the words squashed close and the lines erratic, consulting me at every turn and in no way abashed by my corrections. We even went to the local printer to order some notepaper bearing his name at the top – all part of the plan to nourish pride. No, what Gary detested was the idea that his shortcomings were to be made manifest to strangers, and what he feared was that his bombast might prove inadequate defence.

It was then that I proposed he submit to a session with an educational counsellor who would prepare a report on his abilities. There was a danger of course; the counsellor might well conclude that there were no abilities worth nurturing, but I kept this apprehension to myself, fortified by the belief that these men were professionally disposed to find gold in a slag-heap and saw the encouragement of the young as their *raison d'être*. Gary was all for it. He imagined that if any teacher threatened to give him a hard time, he would be able to brandish a document which proved he was worth bothering about. So we drove to an address in distant Acton, where I abandoned Gary for four hours to a Mr Stonehouse, bearded, shabby, well-intentioned, in a room strewn with papers and books lying on worn sofas and a thinly carpeted floor, beneath a stew of cigarette smoke hanging like ribbons in the air. In a brief chat with me, Stonehouse volunteered the information that he and his wife looked after four foster-children in addition to their own offspring (a son and daughter), ranging in age from seven to seventeen, in consequence of which he understood very keenly what I was up against. It was intended as a warning, but I took it as a signal of fellow-feeling and was absurdly cheered by the thought that I was about to embark on a wholesome enterprise which Stonehouse, at least, would appreciate. I left to spend the hours in a cafeteria, working on a review of Professor Scratch's huge biography of Rabelais while a scared and friendless boy was battling to win for himself an ounce or two of self-confidence. I stopped for a moment to ruminate on the gulf which separated our ambitions, I arranging persuasive words on a page while he grasped for identity. It was bootless reflection. Though I reasoned with myself that the one did not invalidate or cheapen the other, I teetered momentarily on the edge of stark doubt.

Gary emerged jaunty but exhausted. He said he had done well, and Mr Stonehouse had promised to send a report by first post the next day. 'You'll see,' he said. 'You're in for a surprise. Just you wait.' Then, wistfully, 'You will let me see what he says, won't you?'

'I might,' I replied, not unhelpfully or in any spirit of awkwardness, but because I still worried whether the results might not be as joyful as he obviously anticipated. But he looked so guilelessly crestfallen that I relented. 'Yes, I expect I will,' I said.

'You'd better,' said Gary, instantaneously in touch with his aggressive energies. 'It is going to be about me, innit? I've a right to see it. You can't stop me.'

'OK, OK,' I said, slightly unnerved to find myself on the defensive. 'You can read it to me, if you like. Show me what you can do.'

'Yeah, that's right. I might not be able to read every word, mind. Don't expect miracles.'

'Miracles are the least one can ask for. They are sprinkled throughout the day. What I don't expect is resignation or faint-heartedness.'

'There you go again, talking in riddles. No one knows what you're on about half the time. You'd better learn proper English, Brian.'

The two-page report duly arrived two days later. Gary's eyes were set upon the front door during breakfast, waiting for letters to plop on to the carpet. He would have hovered in the street for the postman had even he not felt that excessive enthusiasm might be transparent, unmanly. But he did not disguise impatience when the letters arrived. He rushed to the door, identified the one which concerned him by its long brown envelope, and threw the rest aside as irrelevant. The utter completeness of his self-centredness was alarming but (so I convinced myself) excusable. 'I'll open it,' he announced.

Gary pored over the type-written pages eagerly for a few seconds, then tossed them across the breakfast table at me with a hint of anger behind the impatience. 'It's double dutch,' he said. 'You read it.'

'Why do you give up so soon?' I asked.

'I'm not thick,' he said.

'Nobody said you were. Let's have a look.' The word which stopped Gary like a train buffer was 'performance'. Too many syllables, I mused. 'From Gary's mode of performance in the test situation', the pedagogue had written, 'I have no doubt that he is heavily underfunctioning.' As Gary's pass-port to a future, this was not a bad beginning. I read the next sentence aloud. 'Since his scores were average, this indicates that he is of above-average intelligence, and probably substantially.'

'What's 'e mean, then?' asked Gary.

'He says you're intelligent, but that you don't know how to use your intelligence.'

'Told you so,' he said with triumph, spotting the prize and ignoring the qualification. I read the remainder to myself before giving him a digest. Stonehouse wrote that there were no indications of specific learning disability; Gary was a poor reader because he had read so little, that was all. He then broadened into surmise:

> To attack his problems educationally in the first instance seems to me not only sound, but the only practicable approach. I am sure he would not respond to psychotherapy until he sees his problems much more as his own, rather than as a function of those around him. Even if he were to attend for treatment (which on the evidence is unlikely) he would not use it. Therefore he should take private tuition on a part-time basis, but the school should not be seen by his adults as a major persecuting factor. It appears so to him because, in his present emotional state, he is unable to use what it has to offer.

This was more than I had bargained for. I had not suggested that Gary should be seen by a psychotherapist, and was somewhat taken aback that the possibility was taken for granted by Stonehouse, even if it was afterwards dismissed. To a trained eye, it seemed that Gary was not just a boy in need, but a boy in crisis.

The next paragraph delved further into gloomy foreboding:

> The management problems over the next few years are likely to be considerable. At present, he would seem to be

in the 'honeymoon' phase, characterised by obedience and enthusiasm. This is just beginning to break down, and the development of a more 'real' relationship has started to emerge. In such a relationship, his very evident (and understandable) anger is likely to be inappropriately directed towards you. All your own emotional resources will be called upon to withstand this, if you are to avoid being made into the other half of Gary's internal conflict on the one hand, or a permissive puppet on the other.

A flicker of terror grabbed me as I read this, if only because Stonehouse, after one encounter, saw clearly what I had stupidly or blindly refused to tackle – the fact that I was in danger of being manipulated. That wild unfocused fright passed as soon as I was able to arrange myself and reflect that, of course, manipulation was inevitable and proper. It was the invisible glue which bound any relationship of whatever nature, and I should be glad that Gary could flex his muscles in this way, upon someone who was alive to what was happening and would not therefore react with hostility or ignorance. Perhaps he was a lucky boy to have stumbled into me, though I sternly resisted the sweet and sickly self-satisfaction to which that thought might lead.

Stonehouse finished with an admonition that Gary's home base should be settled finally and that the decision would require Polly Galway's full co-operation, which could be diffi-cult if she was made to feel that she had borne the burden of Gary's upbringing thus far and had shown herself in-adequate. I should not underestimate Gary's perception of our relative value to him and to each other. He was already, wrote Stonehouse, playing the two of us off against each other, determined to extract the best advantage to himself.

'Well, it looks as if you made quite an impression upon Mr Stonehouse,' I said. 'He reckons you're pretty clever.' This was truthful enough, though selective.

'I think I deserve a prize for that,' he said.

'What have you in mind?'

Gary, for the first time that I had noticed, looked rather sheepish, embarrassed, his love of acquisition glaringly exposed. So he did have some moral vision! Or was it merely that he did not trust his strength to cope with refusal? He wanted what he called a music centre (in my generation it had been a gramophone, then a record-player), so he could bring all his records from his nan's. The prospect of loud popular music disturbing the peace at Temple Grove Road was not one I relished, but I acceded to his request on condition he did not use the machine after eleven at night. Gary liked conditions.

Another reason for my compliance was to deflect Gary's attention from a smaller envelope contained within the larger one, addressed to me again but this time marked 'Private'. Clearly Mr Stonehouse was a wise bird; he knew his report would be seen by more eyes than mine, and entrusted his more provocative remarks to secret communication. I read this short letter in a quiet moment half an hour later.

> I think you should recognise [he wrote] that Gary has not yet been rescued. Had you not made the attempt, however, it is virtually certain that his future would be a road to delinquency and the streets, and possibly some quite serious crime. There is within him a propensity to violence which I have rarely seen so pronounced. When I speak of serious crime, I mean rape or murder − or both.

'I don't know what the hell you think you're doing having a pubescent boy in the house. He's nothing to do with you, nothing.'

Helen's voice was never strident. She could make her sharpest criticisms in the gentlest tones, mellifluous, soft, barely causing the cords to vibrate. The knack derived from what was sometimes insultingly called 'breeding', but more accurately could be termed a kind of genetically endowed habit. Helen could identify her antecedents for at least three hundred years, she knew who she was and where she came from. There had been a Lord Chancellor somewhere in the past, and a number of High Court judges. Of none of this did she boast, but it afforded her a degree of quiet comfort. She did not need to raise her voice – it had been raised for her by countless generations. Indeed, she did nothing to excess. She smiled rather than laughed, walked rather than ran, ate smoothly rather than voraciously, no matter how hungry she might be. Her hair was not coiffured, but combed, and she dressed with magnificent simplicity. The lack of ostentation had been apparent even at night, when she had embraced me less like a tempest than a cushion of warm air. In spite of all this, Helen was never dull or boring; she was often giggly and skittish. It was just that she was economical with her assets, so that one always suspected a great deal was held in reserve. It was my fault we had not married, in that I had been unwilling or unable to dig deep and find in her the seams of untapped personality. I had been content to accept her as she was, whereas she had looked to me to renew and invigorate her. I would have wanted marriage as a means of continuing in much the same way as before; she saw it as a route to brutal and exhilarating change. Smothered by my books, I had disappointed her.

Helen and I had never really examined what might have happened had we entered a commitment to one another. As it was, we flayed ourselves, separately, with introspection. I felt, erroneously, that Helen was a fully furnished person, fitted and complete, to whom I could add nothing. Our shared frustration, never alluded to, acted as a faint but persistent magnet which drew her to Temple Grove Road at intervals of a few weeks, when she would stay the night and we would hold each other silently.

She was looking at me now with large luminous eyes, not reproachfully but almost imploringly. She had heard from friends that Gary had moved in, and was curious. Naturally enough, as Gary's one firmest talent was to gather people to him and compel their affection, they had got on well together. But now we were alone, and her remarks were less guarded.

'Of course he has charm,' she said, 'masses of it. It's his only weapon. The boy's never been loved, never been cherished. You can tell at a glance. Charm is his armour, but underneath he is a thoroughly ordinary little boy who needs love, love of a sort you are not equipped to offer. And if you could, you shouldn't. You are wasting your time, Brian, and you are going to make one hell of a fool of yourself. Have you considered how much money and time you will have to spend as the boy grows more and more to look upon you as his guardian? It's not as if you're rich, or idle, so you don't have much of either commodity to spare. He will exploit you and drain you dry, and will not appreciate your efforts because he will consider them his due. What about the evenings? Are you going to cook him up a meal every night like some demented *hausfrau* and feel proud of yourself as you wash his knickers and socks? Or will you take him out to restaurants, to the theatre, to the opera? When you're invited to dinner, will you ask if you can bring your "boy" along? Will he meet academics, and publishers, and actors? You will introduce him to a luxury which he will never be able to attain in adulthood and you will sow the seeds of disillusion which are far more dangerous than if you left him in his own miserable world. If you ask me, there's more chance of his turning criminal with you than without you. Once your so-called benefits are removed, he will fight like a raging bear to replace them, and the resulting chaos will be of your making.'

'Why do you assume the benefits, of which you speak so disparagingly, are transient? What makes you think I will allow them to be removed?'

'Darling, *do* get hold of yourself.' Helen moved towards me and stretched out her hand, touching my knuckles with the tips of her fingers. 'I know you. I know you want a son. But you can't buy them at Sainsbury's and you can't pick them off the streets either. You need to have known Gary since infancy to do him any good, he needs to be essential to you, of your body, not a pawn in an intellectual game you are playing with yourself. It's like masturbation − self-regarding and finite.'

I moved away from Helen and sat down at my desk. The solidity of its warm mahogany permanence and its pervading security, which almost gave odour to the room, had always been a protection against the intrusive messy contingencies of real life. 'I can't just suddenly stop,' I said lamely. 'Events have a way of dictating their own speed. You can't put the brakes on without causing an almighty crash.'

'Typical,' said Helen derisively but not, strangely enough, unkindly. 'You think you are an active agent in all this, whereas you're really a passive participant, someone to whom things happen. If I didn't know you better, I'd say you were pathetic. Others will, so be prepared. Listen, Brian. Gary doesn't belong here, he doesn't fit. Whatever you give him, you will have to take it away again one day so he can return to where he does fit, or, if not return, then find his place, his corner of the world. If you can't see that, then you'd better steel yourself for the alternative, which is a lifetime carrying burdens which are not yours to carry. And I do mean a lifetime. Either stop now, while he still has a chance, and put up with his resentment at being dumped, or see it through to the end, through adolescence, young manhood, unemployment, boredom and futile anger with the world which has not given him what you promised it would. Either abandon him now, or never abandon him. It's as simple as that.'

When Helen left, Gary walked into my study. He tried to

appear nonchalant, shrugged his shoulders and slumped in a chair. 'Did she like me?' he asked.

'Yes, she liked you. Don't worry.' I did not want him to know that he had detractors. Net yet, anyway.

Helen telephoned me the next day. 'Brian,' she said. 'There's something you ought to know. I have been wondering all night how I should tell you, and there's only one way, which is straight. When I unpacked last night, I realised that the spare panties I had with me were missing. There were two. Now I don't want to suggest your precious boy is weird – I'll leave that for you to work out. I would just like to have my knickers back some time, if you don't mind.'

I found them in Gary's room, stuffed at the back of a drawer, crushed into a ball and placed as far out of sight as he could manage.

It was more than faintly ridiculous that I should see Gary off to school on his first day, like some infant equipped with sandwiches, patted at the gate and told to behave, for he was after all nearly as tall as me and his voice was beginning to croak its craggy way towards manhood. At the same time I knew he wanted, in some secret fragile part of himself, to be treated as a child. I compromised. No sandwiches, no waving at the front door, just a degree of concern at breakfast that he should not be late. Gary enjoyed the game too, brushing his teeth in a hurry, galumphing downstairs and swallowing cornflakes as he stood up trying to tie a knot in his school-tie, the whole creating a vision of haste which befitted a recalcitrant, habitually tardy person. It was the role he assigned to himself in the fiction he was playing, and it made him happy. He also resisted having the tie closely knotted up to his collar, but preferred to let the knot hang a little low, with the top button of his shirt undone. A prissy tidiness would have invited too much notice. Besides which, he had never worn a tie before.

When he came home the tie was missing. Gary was sullen and defiant. He had been told that he had to tie it properly, and had straightway ripped it off. He had also been admonished for his brown shoes. 'They want you to get me a pair of new black shoes,' he said.

'We'll get some at the weekend. I'll have a word with the Head and see if you can get away with these until then.'

This pliant attitude of mine produced an explosion of anger which took me completely by surprise. 'Nobody tells me what to do!' he screamed. 'I don't *have* to do anything. My mum was the only one who told me what I *had* to do, and I'm not taking it from anyone else.' He spat the words out, with clenched bared teeth, jutting chin, and finger jabbing the air in front of my face. I proffered a hand to his shoulder as an instrument of calm, but it was immediately shrugged off, and Gary tore out of the room, slamming the door with such violence that the house shook.

For a moment I stood alone, in awe at the sudden unleashing of potent forces and with considerable misgivings. I should not have been surprised; I had observed the dark rumblings of suppressed rage ever since our evening at the cinema, and could not have expected, rationally, that they would never erupt. What did they presage? What was their cause? What further banks of contained explosiveness lurked within him? And what was their epicentre? To these questions I had no answers, but I was alerted by the reference to his mother, pulled out at a moment of stress and defiance. What, indeed, had she done that his memory of her could not be summoned in peaceful reflection, but only surged forward in tandem with his wrath? Was she the talisman invoked to keep the enemy at bay, or was she in fact the enemy disguised as lover, the ultimate traitor?

I resolved not to tamper with these raw mysteries. Upstairs, I found Gary listening to records and smoking a cigarette. I turned the record-player off.

'What d'you do that for?'

'I want to talk to you. I can't shout above that din.'

'What about?' He was still prickly, unmalleable, drawing deeply on the cigarette by way of overt challenge.

'Tell me what you did in school,' I said.

'Nothing to tell. It's a shitty school and I'm not going back.'

'Don't be daft, Gary. You've only just started. Nobody said it would be easy.'

'If you think it's so good, *you* go there.'

'Did you learn anything?'

'Only rubbish.'

'What classes did you have?'

'Fuck knows. I don't know what they're talking about half the time.' He kept his eyes averted and continued stubbing out his cigarette long after it was extinguished. I lit one myself, and walked to the window, gazing out at the leaves, prematurely blown off straining branches by an autumn gust. When I turned back, Gary had thrown some exercise books on the bed. 'Look at these, if you want,' he said.

They were from a mathematics class and bore two pages of oblongs and triangles meticulously drawn and coloured. Each diagram was accompanied by a tick in red biro. 'This is good,' I said.

'Yeah, well I can't do any more.'

'Why ever not?' I asked.

'They said I've got to bring me own ruler and pencils, and something called a compass. I haven't got any, have I? Why did they have to say so in front of everyone? All the other kids had all this junk with them. I was the only one who had to borrow from someone else. Felt a right charlie, didn't I. It's all your fault. You should have got them for me.'

So he had been humiliated! I wondered at the crass insensitivity of teachers who recognise a fragile tentative confidence and proceed to demolish it with gleeful precision.

'I've got an old set of protractors and things in the cellar somewhere,' I said. 'You can use those until we buy you a new set.' He looked at me at last.

'So you reckon I've done all right?' he queried.

'Of course you have. Kids who've been doing maths for years would be glad to draw like that. You've got a lot to catch up on, mind, but you can do it.'

'I'll tell the teacher I've got to bring home my books every day,' he said. 'I'll say you said so. They can't say no if you said so, can they? You can tell me if they're all right.'

It was then that I noticed his knee was grazed. It transpired that he had stormed out of the classroom, pursued by a teacher whose authority had been frustrated, and had fallen and injured himself. The school nurse wanted to give him an injection against tetanus on the spot, but Gary would have nothing to do with it and the nurse had thought better than to attempt enforcement.

'They want me to go and have a jab in the hospital,' he said, 'but I ain't going nowhere near any hospital. They kill people in those places.'

'They also save people,' I said. 'But never mind. It's not important. There's a doctor round the corner who can give you a quick jab.'

'You've got to come with me,' he said. Gary was clearly terrified of hospitals and doctors, probably because he associated them with people being taken away from him. His grandmother was always 'poorly', and I could only surmise what hospitals had meant to his mother. Only a straitjacket would have kept him down had the school authorities insisted on injecting him. At the doctor's, Gary clung on to me with white knuckles as the needle was prepared. His eyes were desperate. I felt a glow of warm regard for him at that moment, the source of which was confused. I admired his courage, yes, for he had manifestly to overcome obstacles within himself as well as those hurled at him from outside,

46

but I was also happy that the ire which fuelled his mighty obstinacy had subsided.

That evening before he went to bed he asked if he could call his father in Birmingham. It was a fruitless attempt at connection. His father spoke to him, but could not indicate when he might be coming to see him, nor could he impart any hint of enthusiasm that he might want to. Gary's face was a portrait of abject hopelessness as he put the phone down, a vision of calamitous disappointment. He said nothing, and I was not inclined to make the usual feeble excuses on behalf of a man who ought, I was sure, to have manufactured some interest.

I sat with Gary for five minutes before he went to sleep. It was a ritual he wanted to maintain and which I was ready to honour.

'What's a godfather do?' he asked.

'A godfather is supposed to sponsor a child and see to it that he is educated according to the moral precepts of the Church. But most of the time the godfather merely acts as an insurance in the background, someone who can help out if, well, if the parents can't manage for some reason. Why do you ask?'

'I didn't know how to explain to the other kids who you were. It doesn't make much sense. Someone said you must be my godfather. I said yeah, that's right, that's what he is, my godfather. But I want to know if it's right.' He paused for a few seconds, then busied himself with setting the alarm, as if to diminish the import of what he was about to say, to demonstrate by association the mechanical triviality of his thoughts.

'Does that mean', he said, 'that if anything happened to my nan, you'd look after me?'

'Yes, that's more or less what it means.'

He grinned. I got up to leave. 'By the way,' I said, 'I've given Helen back her things. I don't suppose there's any point in my asking you why you took them.'

47

He shrugged and pouted, implying that he hadn't a clue, and could not be bothered to assist me in any investigation of motive. As I closed the door behind me and was safely beyond his catching any reaction from me, he said, quietly but with emphasis, 'She doesn't belong here, anyway.'

The strength and finality of his determination sent a momentary chill through me.

THREE

OTHER PEOPLE IN the house accepted the new arrangement with grace, sometimes with amusement, never, I
am happy to say, with resentment. The most amused was
Gertrude, a woman of vague past and even vaguer age, who
might have been fifty, seventy, or anywhere in between.
Having no passport, and having long since torn up her birth
certificate with delight, Gertrude deflected teasing enquiries
with practised aplomb. She had been twice married (once
legally) and twice widowed, each time to a man called John
(she distinguished them as 'John No. 1' and 'John No. 2'), and
had come to me through the influence of friends in the wake
of her second bereavement. The intention was that she
should stay for a few weeks while she sorted herself out, but
the sorting-out had become a protracted endeavour with little
sign of an outcome. Nobody minded, for Gertrude, with her
flaming red hair, her Russian-French-Hungarian origins (we
suspected they were really rooted in Hove), and her outrageous stories of former plenty, was an asset and a joy. Gary
had never dreamt such an exotic person was possible, and
listened to her, entranced, as she told him how her home was
really in Venice. I did not like to spoil the fun by pointing out
that she had stayed in an hotel there and did not speak a word
of Italian. Never having had children ('I would have strangled
them at birth, dear'), she was not burdened with experience

of youth, and therefore took to Gary as just another camp-occupant, and an ideal audience. It certainly would not have occurred to her to think his presence in any way odd; all audiences were good, of whatever age and from whatever source.

The others were less often there, yet became more involved in Gary's fate. Like many actors of his age, Stuart was ambitious, extrovert and self-confident. His long years of struggle in repertory theatre had, he thought, earned him the right to demand a reward for his talents, and he measured this reward by the number of autograph-hunters who took the trouble to seek him out. Some TV work had made his face familiar and it was rumoured that he was destined for a bright future. He had presence and style, his handsome appearance carefully nurtured, his manner relaxed and gracious, as of one who knew how to put admirers at their ease. His rough beginnings in the tawdry streets of Bermondsey and Camberwell were quick to manifest their influence, however, and Stuart liked to give the impression that he was 'of the people'; he was happiest in a pub or wine-bar, swapping stories with the locals. Other actors noticed that, when a break in shooting occurred, Stuart would invite them to join him and the technicians in a drink at the nearest bar, as if to indicate that he alone was able to bridge the two worlds and make contact between them less embarrassing for both. I had cause to expect his relations with Gary would be smooth and congenial; at twenty-eight he was not so divorced in age from the boy as I was, and with the actor's nose for character would doubtless intuit the springs of behaviour which to others might seem unfathomable. I anticipated an ally. No more than Gertrude would Stuart regard Gary as a troublesome intruder.

Stuart was not married to Josie, but, in the manner of the day, 'lived with' her. She, also in the acting profession, led a life as peripatetic as his, which made the periods of their cohabitation brief and sporadic. If she found herself in London at the same time as Stuart, she moved in to Temple Grove Road for a week, a month, or a day, so that she was almost a resident. I had long ago surrendered the attempt to explain to outsiders that I did not run a lodging-house, but that we all shared accommodation. When bread was in danger of running out, someone went and bought it. Nobody kept a count of who had bought what, a rule I insisted upon after another actor, who had passed through for the shortest time, wrote his initials on his eggs. Josie, an effervescent, loquacious girl, anxious to please, was as happy with this arrangement as Stuart, and when I was out of town the two of them would give parties and entertain friends to dinner in the knowledge that the house was as much their home as mine. In a way, more so; I had fallen into the habit of treating the place like an hotel, somewhere to sleep, bathe, and turn on the telly. All this, I realised, would have to change in no small degree. I would need to be at home more often, Stuart and Josie would have subtly to make space for Gary in the disposition of their time at the house.

A week after Gary started at school, they both arrived fresh from engagements in the provinces. They had not yet unpacked and were having coffee in the kitchen when Gary burst in, tore off his tie and threw it over a chair, and sat proprietorially on his favourite chair at the table. 'Who's gonna get me a cup of tea, then?' he asked.

'Don't you think we'd better be introduced first,' said Josie, rather primly and uncharacteristically, taken aback.

'I'm Gary. I live here.'

'I'm Josie, and that is Stuart. So do we.'

'Oh yeah, Brian told me something about you.' He lit a cigarette, the nonchalance so perfect Stuart would have done well to take notes. I had of course long since told Gary of the two arrivals, and he knew well enough that they would be in the house. He had had all the journey home to prepare himself for the meeting, and had evidently decided on the cocky demeanour, leaving the charm for later.

'Aren't you a bit young to smoke?' said Josie.

'Brian lets me. What's it to you?'

'Nothing, nothing. I'm just surprised, that's all. You'll make your lungs black and putrid before you're twenty.'

'They're *my* lungs.'

Stuart intervened. 'Come on, son,' he said, 'Josie's only being friendly. Cool it.' The patronising approach was rescued, as it were, by the vulgar colloquialism, that steady cocktail of Stuart's which made him so popular. It worked.

'I've seen you on the telly, haven't I?'

'Maybe. Do you watch much?'

'Not much else to do, is there.' It wasn't a question. Gary attempted to disguise his interest. 'You didn't have a very big part, or I would have remembered.'

Stuart laughed. 'There you go. Fame and fortune down the plug, chased by a thirteen-year-old cynic!'

'I'm not thirteen, I'm fourteen [Gary added a few months to advance his impending birthday]. And what's a cynic?'

'Right now, someone who deflates an actor's ego, and about time, too. But don't tell anyone.' Stuart placed his forefinger on the right of his nose, in a conspiratorial gesture. Josie was out of sight pouring hot water from the kettle into the tea-pot. Gary grinned.

'Will you take me to watch?'

'Watch what? You mean, to the studio when we're filming?'

'Yeah, that's right. Will you?'

'I don't see why not. But it will have to be a day when you're off school. Brian's told me that you are doing well, and I am not going to encourage you to take any time off. He'd have me minced up for breakfast.'

'No, he wouldn't. I'll handle him. He's easy. Besides, I often get time off. I can arrange it.'

'All the same, you can come, with Brian's permission, if we're on location on a Saturday. I'll talk to him about it.'

Josie came in with the tea. She had always been a tactile woman, and once said she could never trust anyone who flinched at a touch. It was her litmus test. She placed a hand on Gary's forearm, looked him challengingly in the eye, and smiled broadly. 'We're all going to get on like a house on fire, aren't we?'

'Don't see why not,' said Gary. 'Let's have some tea, then.'

Every Tuesday and Friday afternoon Gary's class played football, an activity he affected to despise. This was in itself bewildering, as one might have expected him to embrace the opportunity for ritualised violence and to welcome a chance to display. Perhaps he was acting on the fruits of intro-spection and now wanted to avoid an occasion which might remove the inhibitions and spread open the path to un-control. But this was speculation. He had shown no signs of any such introspection. His tutor, whom he went to see on those sporting afternoons, was to spot the clues to self-awareness much faster than I could.

Phoebe Yorke was an earnest, warm-hearted spinster who devoted her life to the principle of education as freeing of the spirit. Bespectacled and dumpy, clad in richly coloured jumpers, she awakened the spectre of left-wing radicalism, then proceeded to dilute it with exquisite manners and tem-perance. She was soft-spoken, not strident, bearing her phil-osophy with decorum. Phoebe was at permanent war with schools, which, she declared, confused the learning of skills with the induction of codes. Spelling and writing were pointless unless they released talent and spawned an indi-vidual personal view of the world. They were tools to be wielded for chiselling a soul, not bricks to build an obedient conformity. She set about the task of chiselling Gary's soul with relish and devotion.

He journeyed to her top-floor flat in Islington by himself, using the bus route. (Again, for unexplained reasons which could well have been important, he refused to travel anywhere by underground train.) The fact that he never missed a session was in itself encouraging, though he sometimes sat in sullen silence, declining to co-operate, and once insisted the curtains be drawn and the lesson be conducted in artificial light. He loudly complained that she should have a lift installed at the house and would puff and pant for ten minutes in an armchair before allowing the session to proceed, thus drawing attention to the sacrifice he was making in turning up at all and at the same time establishing his power to promote events according to a pace he dictated. Phoebe was used to this and resisted the temptation to scold.

'Gary's predicament', she told me, 'is that he still needs what he evidently missed as a baby – fun, games, and acceptance. I mean that a baby is appreciated even for the things which are later called dirty, smelly, rude, and is loved unconditionally. Heaven knows what happened in the past, but he is still testing whether appreciation might be withdrawn if he is objectionable. He has got to recapture his babyhood and get through it with urgent speed, for he feels clearly enough that he is on the threshold of manhood and wants to enter that new world fully prepared.'

'Can he do it?'

'Yes, it is not too late by any means. There will be some overlap which will disconcert him, but he looks to you to help him on the journey. His main outstanding motivating factor is to shine and be clever like you, not for its own sake so much as to impress others. But he has such strong negative reactions to any failure along the way that he has made the going very tough for himself. He has also begun to learn how to cope with social situations. He boasts about the people he has met

54

with you, the people he knows. The showing off is quite valid, since he has something to show, but the line between sharing exciting experiences and flaunting them is slightly drawn. I think Gary is learning where that line is located. He is relying on mathematics, the one area where he knows he has best possibilities of shining. He takes enormous pains to make his maths book look good, is meticulous with colouring and general layout, and resents my interference in his field of achievement. If he finds something difficult to work out and I come with a suggestion, he gets upset and rejects what he calls my stupid way of doing it. Next time round, he will quietly adopt my way as long as the capitulation can be disguised. He is irritable and impatient, often abusive to me, especially when he needs help but hates accepting it. His physical aggression towards anything which gets in his way, at these times, is only just controlled. Like deliberately wiping a biro on his shirt, or grinding a pencil point, which I had sharpened, hard into the wall, or pulling a stiff drawer of the desk in and out as noisily as possible. He totally rejects other subjects because they interrupt his progress on the one subject in which he has sunk his hopes. He is desperately consolidating and testing out his one real school success.'

'Nevertheless, he will have to struggle with the reading, or his failures will multiply.'

'I know. He has improved enormously, but he invents obstacles by choosing things to read which are dauntingly difficult, and rejecting my suggestions. I am amazed how easily he reads the technical maths terms, so the ability is there, thwarted only by his low tolerance of frustration.'

'Does he have any insight into his problems?'

'Yes, though he is far too frightened to talk about it. I have never ventured to interpret − that could light a dangerous spark − but have limited myself to the occasional observation inviting him to comment. He won't. When I told him, for example, that he wasn't *really* angry with the pencil for making a mistake, and that something else must be making him cross, he ignored me and went on grinding the pencil into the wall with renewed vigour. There was written on his face, I don't think I exaggerate, the most tortured, tormented struggle with dark excoriating thoughts. He was remembering something awful. I quickly changed the subject.'

'Will he ever open up?'

'Not yet. As I said, he is suspended between babyhood and adulthood, he is a very immature vulnerable boy with a useful masking veneer of sophistication. He shows signs that he will carry on to good avail but he will use heavily the resources of many sympathetic people along the way. He won't show his need yet, he won't reveal that he is finding it hard to believe in himself, and why should he? He has to be able to cope with something before he will admit to any need in helping to cope with it. He foists his feelings on to others to avoid facing the sadness and anger he harbours towards himself. The needing bits of Gary are completely raw, they hurt if touched. He will back off if I assist too readily and expose his helplessness. Only he can change this way of being. I can't change it for him, and neither can you. As he realises his own depression and the self-destructive side of his character, he will need confidence in his own abilities to battle with them. There are tiny tiptoe steps in this direction. Let me give you an example. We play word-games as a way towards stimulating an interest in reading. He usually chucks the paper to the floor in a rage if he looks like losing. But once he went to the trouble to find a word in the dictionary in order to win a point. It was the first time he had admitted to needing help from outside, and I was glad, relieved, overjoyed in fact, that the book gave him that help. Now, he will offhandedly ask how to spell a word or check that his spelling of it is correct, and I will reply in an equally off-hand manner so as not to make it too obvious that the omnipotent Gary has capitulated. It's quite a delicate operation, I can tell you.'

'I hope it's not too much for you. I don't want you to be drained by this relentless tension. It should not be *your* problem, after all.'

'Don't worry. I'll let you know. There was one moment, I suppose I should tell you, there was a moment when I felt quite scared. It was after one of the drawer-shifting episodes, which were getting me down because the clatter was like an insult to my endeavours. Stupid of me, I know, unforgivably insensitive, but I felt for once that he should show a bit of sensitivity too, that my comfort ought to figure in his scheme of things. It's too soon – the taking is at the stage of a very young child, for whom there can be no comparative giving as yet. Anyway, I told him to stop the racket or I would terminate the session and send him home. He stared at me across the table, a thin, menacing, ice-cold stare, for long seconds, perhaps a minute, during which I swear his eyes changed colour and focus, as if a new person, a new unwholesome personage were being summoned up from deep within him, or indeed had invaded him from somewhere in the room, from a source I could not see or imagine. The childishness had evaporated in a flash, had been replaced by a sinisterly aged experienced force. I told myself, Phoebe, those eyes are like shafts of fire. Be careful. That's not Gary, that's a man possessed. Watch him, Phoebe, look and watch. He's immolating you, reducing your flesh to dust. I returned his stare, transfixed. It was I who had to look away. When I looked back, there were beads of sweat on his brow and a trickle of saliva dribbled from the corner of his mouth. I don't want to worry you, Mr Masters, but you must not lose sight of the tremendous contest that boy is fighting. Whether he wins or loses, it will be done in front of you. You will see it.'

Helen's misgivings and the dire warnings of two pedagogues ought probably to have made me pause. But Gary himself seemed so visibly to blossom in a kind of rapid self-congratulatory radiance that I was happy to dismiss gloomy prognostications from my mind and trust in what I could see. Gary was obliging and obedient, trustful, gregarious, growing daily with his reliable decent routine into a boy of solid hopes. His uncomplicated relationship with Stuart Perrott was proving to be part of the cement of his reconstruction, for Stuart's mild fame and evident fondness for him fuelled his need to have something to vaunt and brag about. Earlier, other boys in Temple Grove Road had grown irritated with Gary and his fantasies. Boys will not tolerate blatant lies for long, and they had challenged Gary's tall stories, thus embarrassing him and rejecting a friendship on such false terms. A boy who has little to be proud of must invent something, but the risk he so takes is massive – his position in the hierarchy may be assailed, even demolished, if he is found out. Gary had been lying to adults for years and had never been questioned. His grandmother believed everything. The stories became more and more fantastic, Gary's grasp of the line between fact and fiction more and more tenuous. In the streets of Ladbroke Grove, however, he was not believed. The shock undermined him, astonished him, probably even churned his frustration. He had never before had to face denial or justify himself; he did not see the need, because he had forgotten that he was lying in the first place. All this had changed. He boasted about knowing Stuart and did not have to cover up. His friends had seen him greet Stuart, run errands for him, discourse with him at the gate in gentle camaraderie. Stuart was his badge with the neighbourhood gangs.

Josie rarely collided with Gary. Helen had not visited since the day Gary stole her panties. Gertrude kept herself apart at the top, except when entertaining us with fantasies. So the household was highly artificial – almost exclusively male, with a pubescent boy trying to manufacture a filial relationship with me and a lateral comradely back-slapping relationship with Stuart. In the streets he was just one other boy who had to be home at a certain time. The fact that 'home' was unconventional was beside the point. It was a focus which looked to him as if it would stay constant, as long as he kept the rules. This he was more than ready to do.

When we had visitors, Josie would come to help with the cooking, and Gary would be eagerly at her elbow in the kitchen, peeling potatoes, mixing, or simply washing up. He was agreeable with guests, spoke when invited to but was otherwise diffident and respectful. It was all too good to be true. He went up to bed when told, having politely saluted everyone present. People started to compliment me as though he was my son. This, oddly enough, embarrassed me, although it should have been as clear to me as it obviously was to Gary that I was being groomed for just such a role.

There was one oddity of his behaviour which caused me no concern, yet suggested deep currents of volition which could be puzzling. Gary was scrupulously clean. He bathed at least twice a day, in a long luxuriating session in the tub, and was forever washing his hands. This was to be welcomed in so far as it was, I suspected, more usual for a boy of his age to be encrusted with grime and reluctant to remove it. I remembered an American girl I had once met who travelled with two suitcases, one of which was entirely stocked with soaps, shampoos, towels and tissues. She wiped her hands compulsively and cleaned her teeth every hour. Gary was nowhere near this state of neurosis, yet I did wonder about the cause of excessive cleanliness in him and hoped that it would gradually be discarded along with other nagging residues of peculiar conduct. He had at least given up trying to shove unwanted food on to other people's plates, which I had interpreted as a manifestation of the same desire to remove a 'soiling' item.

The school required him, along with other pupils, to bring

home a daily time-table initialled by each teacher, as proof of attendance. On one of these the headmaster wrote at the bottom, 'You're winning!', a curiously uplifting message, not because he was necessarily right, but because he maintained his interest in the attempt. However, I did notice one day that a signature had been forged, or so I thought, presumably by Gary. I could not be sure, so I did not pursue the possibility with him. It was a small worry which I preferred not to pick at.

Gary's smoking was another matter. He could not afford, on the modest allowance I permitted him, to buy more than a couple of packets a week, and yet he was never without a supply. He had asked whether he could forgo school lunches, which were revolting (he said) and go to his grandmother's for a mid-day meal. As other children did the same, there seemed no reason to object. I suspected that she gave him cigarettes as a matter of course, and determined that I would speak to her about it and try to gain her support in stemming the flow. Cigarettes *per se* did not offend so much as the circumventing of a regulation, namely that he should learn to 'make ends meet'. In the mean time, I said that I wanted him to give up the habit, and promised that I would do so as well. I thought that if it was a shared deprivation he might enjoy it rather than resent it. I suggested that he cut down little by little, until he was only smoking five a day, then three, then one, then none at all. Gary grabbed the opportunity with what appeared to be genuine intent, and when the day came for us both to abandon smoke altogether he made no attempt to renege on his promise and withstood the sacrifice bravely.

Much later I had to acknowledge that Gary was smoking secretively, on the street with his mates or in the park when he took the dog for a walk. What mattered was that he did not want me to witness his fall, and there was never any threat to smoke in the house. This, I thought, was an accomplishment I should not denigrate, so I pretended not to know he was quietly cheating.

Was I perhaps afraid to confront him, just as his grand-mother had all her life been afraid? The forged signature on his school time-table and the furtive smoking were each a reason for conflict and ought to have led to plain speaking. Gary was undeniably a powerful will — one did not want to put it to the test gratuitously. I convinced myself that I was being wise and pragmatic in letting these things pass. His progress in every other direction was so good yet so fragile that it was not worth the risk of regression just for the sake of a petty display of authority on my part.

I was also cheered by Gary's willingness to look after the dog. Of course, one of the reasons he was so ready to take the animal for a walk was that it afforded him the chance for a surreptitious smoke. Nevertheless, part of the purpose was to save me a chore, and the closeness between boy and dog was a positive advance in Gary's ability to gratify any emotion other than anger. The dog slept on his bed, accompanied him to the bus-stop in the morning, and when Gary alighted from the bus in the late afternoon, there he was again shaking his little body with excitement. Nicky soon became known in the neighbourhood as 'Gary's dog', which on all the evidence he now was.

Gary was popular with the shopkeepers for his cheerful breezy manner and readiness to help. He soon became known at the old people's residence beyond the back garden, where some twenty elderly widows and widowers lived in separate flats controlled by a warden. Gary offered to help prepare their jumble-sale, and took charge of one of the stalls, selling second-hand records. So urgent was his keenness that he raced out into the street to kidnap passers-by and drag them in, and moreover he would not let them go before they consented to buy something or other. The old people thought this cute and charming, they thought Gary was 'a card', 'a wag', they wanted to adopt him as their mascot. His youthful exuberance was a tonic for them, and I must admit that the proximity of extreme old age and headstrong adolescence was touching to behold. It made one ruminate on that long passage of time, yet all too sickeningly short, which separated the two, the heavy baggage of memories carried by the old and the frank openness of the young, ready to receive experience. They seemed so odd together, contingent, incongruous, but at the same time natural, connected by the solid cord of years. I felt pleased that Gary was bringing a smile to those sad sallow faces.

One old lady in particular, Mrs Hardcastle, had a soft spot for Gary. It had started quite otherwise. She had complained that his music blared out of his bedroom at the back, with the window wide open, and disturbed her budgerigar.

'I dunno what the old cow's on about,' Gary had said, with a dismissive defiant derision which was deeply unattractive.

'She's going on about the noise you make, and she's not an old cow. You haven't even met her.'

'Don't want to, neither.'

'Well, I think you should. Go and see her. Apologise, make friends.'

'There's nothing for me to apologise *for*. Apologise? That's for the birds. You won't catch me apologising, not for no one.'

'Gary, an apology is not a submission. It's not a surrender. You're not Samson about to be shorn of his strength. It's a connection, a contact, an enfolding by one person of another person's vulnerability. It's a gift.'

'You mean I've got to give her something?'

'Only your company, your voice, your being there. You can sweep away her irritation by being attentive to her. To say you're sorry only means that you are thinking about her desires and concerns, when she in her loneliness assumes she is the only person to think of them. It doesn't mean you are laying yourself on a slab and inviting her to castrate you or something. Don't be afraid.'

'Afraid? Don't make me laugh, Brian. All right, I'll go and

see her. Just hope she apologises too, for interfering with my life. It can't be all me what does the apologising.'

Thus began their extraordinary friendship. Mrs Hardcastle, eighty-eight, frail in body but high-spirited, white curly hair and shoulders hunched by sixty years of coughing, false teeth clattering in repose as if she were always munching an imaginary toffee, and Gary, cheeky, ebullient, vigorous and as yet unformed for life. Their mutual hostility had evaporated, as I suspected it would, within minutes. Gary became a regular visitor, popping round for a cup of tea with the old lady and fixing her light-bulbs (Mrs Hardcastle had a bizarre fear of electricity, presuming it to be floating around the room unharnessed if the light-bulb was missing, and she could barely summon the courage to turn on a switch, never knowing what it might produce, despite the evidence of years; she also habitually knocked the furniture with a spoon as she passed, as children rattle railings with a stick). When we were shopping together, Gary never failed to mention her. 'Don't forget to buy some biscuits for old Mrs H. And she likes walnut cake. Get her a walnut cake.' It was her idea to organise the jumble-sale, and his encouragement which sustained her.

I was not therefore altogether surprised to discover a note from her two weeks later, containing what I imagined might be an invitation to tea. This is what I read:

Dear Mr Masters,

I feel horrible at having to write this but Gary is taking money out of my pocket (proof). Two Wednesdays ago I had exactly £2 and some change in my purse, went to shop, going home only £1 in it. I thought I had lost it but really didn't know how I could. So I left it at that. On the Wednesday just gone I had £1.50 in my purse. I went to the bakers after Gary had been and there was only 50p there. Now I thought hard because I knew I had £1.50 that morning. So I started to think, is Gary taking it, as he is the only one around. So I am sorry but I thought if I see him today I'll set a trap, which I did. I took my purse out of my pocket and put a £1 note and some change in my pocket. Now the £1 note is gone and the change only left in my pocket. I have the number of the £1 note here. I was going to ring you but I thought again. I suppose by the time you get back he will have spent the £1. I will not say anything to him as quite honestly being as he is, caught out, I would be afraid in the house on my own. Now I know this is silly but I am going to leave it up to you as I think it should not go on any further. But you can see from events it is Gary. I only wish you were here and he would be caught.

Elsie Hardcastle

It was exactly like a hammer-blow between my shoulder-blades. I reeled. I read it all through again with the foolish notion that I must have misunderstood something crucial. Weak with shock and disillusion, I sat pondering for a long while, on the hurt done to Mrs Hardcastle, on the fear she expressed, on Gary's deceit and amorality, which I still was inclined to regard as fundamentally innocent in the true sense of the word – that he did not intend, *could* not intend, actually to do harm. It must surely be a terrible kind of blankness, a gap in his understanding of the world, a missing component in the puzzle of his character. Theft, I supposed, was a common enough feature of delinquency. It was even said by some psychiatrists to be a craving for love. I was in no mood to assess the validity of such a theory. I needed urgently to work out how to deal with its practical consequences. That Mrs Hardcastle was afraid of the boy meant that she too, despite their warm convivial relationship, had seen the mark of a sinister and dangerous warp within him, which she had tried to tame by her trust and her joy.

There was no way to avoid a confrontation with Gary. Part

of me did not want to avoid it, wanted on the contrary to exorcise this demon, tear it out of his breast and hang it up for both of us to gaze at and neutralise. At the same time I knew this was an unlikely outcome. I sat at my desk and waited.

Gary came in from school an hour later, bright-eyed and cheerful. He walked into my study, sat in the armchair and opened his maths book.

'Look at this,' he said. 'I got top marks. Well, nearly. Some swot got more than me, but the teacher gave me loads of ticks. Just look! Gary rules, OK!'

I took the book. It was true. He had made stirling progress and had cause to rejoice. 'That's terrific,' I said. 'I knew you could do it.'

'Well, then. Are we going to celebrate? You going to get me a present or something?'

'Not just yet. There's something we have to talk about first.'

'Go ahead. Talk.'

'I've had a letter from Mrs Hardcastle.'

'I expect she wants me to go and see her.'

'No, Gary. In fact, she would probably rather you didn't at the moment.'

'Why? What's up?'

'She's lost some money. Money that was in her pocket and that's gone. Not once, but three times.'

Gary's demeanour changed abruptly. I thought for a second that he blushed, but this was quickly superseded by a wave of pale fury which swept down from his forehead to his neck. He did not look at me, but stared at the ground between his feet and spoke intensely and quickly, almost to himself.

'The bitch,' he muttered. 'The bitch. Accusing me. No one accuses me. *No one.*'

'Don't talk like that,' I said. 'You know she's not a bitch, she's your friend. And she hasn't accused you. One only accuses an enemy one wishes to attack. You're not an enemy, but you have disappointed her. And there's no point denying it, because she doesn't just suspect, she knows. So do I.'

Gary flashed a look of despair at me which opened a chink of vision into his heart. 'Why do you have to believe something against me? Eh? Why? You're just like all the rest, you are. Why don't you check? What makes you think I am in the wrong, without even asking? *You're* accusing me, too.'

'Tell me what happened, then.'

'Oh, what's the use! You should have left me alone, that's what you should have done, left me where I was. I was doing all right before you interfered. And you would've been better off, wouldn't you? Without me and all this crap.' He made a move to get up.

'Sit down,' I said. 'It doesn't help to get all worked up. We can only decide what to do by talking about it, sensibly and calmly.'

'You talk, if you like. I ain't got nothing to talk about. You shouldn't *accuse* me, that's all.'

'This is what I propose. I don't intend to take it out of your pocket money, that would be too easy. You have to learn that forgiveness is earned. You want to feel all right with Elsie Hardcastle again. You want to feel all right with me. You think that all we have to do is *say* it's all right and it will be. That's not the way it works, Gary. That's not genuine. It's not real. The thoughts will not go away because we want them to. *You* have got to get rid of them and replace them with other thoughts. This is how you do it. Get a Saturday job, helping the milkman or serving at the shop or cleaning windows, anything, and take out of your earnings what Elsie has lost and give it to her yourself. The rest you will give to me to lodge in your bank account. When it's all over, you will see that you have made things better by *doing* something instead of expecting other people to do things.'

'What if I say no.'

'You won't. You will want to do it.'

'I can't work in a shop. I'm not good enough at counting.'

'Well then, you can weed somebody's garden. And make sure whoever it is you work for comes to me and tells me how much they're paying you for it.'

'You want blood, don't you?'

I ignored the remark. I noticed that the admission that he could not count well was the first indication I had ever heard from him that he was wanting in some way. It was like a substitute for the admission of guilt which he could not face, and for the apology which could not be wrenched from him, though he knew it ought to be.

'Can I go out now?'

'No homework?'

'I'll do it before I go to bed.'

'OK. Off you go. You've got to earn that money this weekend, mind. No dithering.'

As he opened the door of my study to leave, he did not turn, but spoke with his back to me. 'My mum would have known what to do,' he said. 'She would have thumped me.'

Gary worked every Saturday for the next few weeks, clearing gardens of autumn leaves and washing cars. The cars, representatives of gleaming sensual power, were a delight to him, but the littered lawns were another matter. He begged to be let off the chore, and when this was refused, implored me to help him. I don't think he really wanted someone else to assist in the sweeping of leaves. Much more important was that he should not feel isolated in his disgrace. If I were there with him, then the fault could not have been so bad after all; moreover, the solitary condition of the punished sinner is uniquely hard to bear — as if one's transgression were made visible, tangible, an object of curiosity and discussion merely by virtue of its being set apart in this way. The offender as outcast, that is the unendurable part of it. Gary wanted me to help him sweep leaves as proof that he was not in exile. I did not oblige.

He paid Elsie Hardcastle out of his earnings, without once admitting the reason for the payment. It was as though he were doing her a favour. Neither did she raise the matter. They resumed friendship as before, with perhaps more circumspection on her part in the degree of latitude she allowed him.

I subsequently discovered that this had not been Gary's only improbity. Josie had said she would pay for him to have a haircut, gave him £5 and said he should bring back the change. He returned with £1. The next time she was at the hairdresser's it was revealed that Gary had been charged a special juvenile rate of £2. He had therefore pocketed an extra £2 at Josie's expense. The offence was not grave in itself, but the indifference to ordinary justice, which demanded he should be grateful to Josie rather than exploit her generosity, was depressing.

Once he had paid off Elsie, Gary continued to work and to hand me the proceeds, which I carefully banked for him. One day I found on my desk a bottle of wine, a decent claret which he had doubtless noticed was among my favourites – Château de By – beneath which was a note:

Dear Brian,
   Thankyou for being such a good dad to me this is a tocon of my grattude out of my third weeks wagers
                                        Lots off love
                                                    Gary

My first, miserable, thought was that he had evidently not surrendered all his earnings if there was sufficient left for him to buy a bottle of wine (and what else, I wondered?). Even if true, this was an unworthy reflection. Here, surely, was a gesture as potent and as graceful as an entreaty. It was Gary's first attempt to prise himself into the world of ethical responsibilities which was so foreign to him and, presumably, so forbidding. He had, after all, glimpsed the nature of relationships which obtained at Temple Grove Road, so unlike the lawlessness of his grandmother's abode where he had simply gobbled up all the kindnesses bestowed upon him without attaching any value to them, and he had now decided he wanted to be gathered into this new world of reciprocal exchange. He did not want to be a maverick, banished to a lonely corner where rules did not apply, answerable to no one and responsible for nothing. The parameters I was trying gingerly to set around his conduct were perhaps not resented – they gave him a strong fibrous tug towards a society wherein he saw his future might lie. He was clinging to the rope however much it might tear his hands.

There was another word in his note which gave me pause – the misspelt 'gratitude'. I was not a little ashamed that such a word should be used, for it made me realise that I was looking for it. The expectation of gratitude was, I thought, a regrettable emotion, belittling and degrading any gift, and peculiarly inimical to the giver. No real parent would allow space in his heart for any such base calculation. Gary's message stood before me like a reproach, and clarified the essential falsity of our positions *vis-à-vis* one another. He was not my son, and I was not therefore beholden to him, yet I seemed to be wanting appreciation from him that I had taken the trouble to *pretend* we were bound by filial obligation. Was it, as Helen had bluntly suggested, no more than a game, a charade to embellish my arid, featureless, steady life? Was I *using* this boy's fractured psyche to experiment with the subtle gradations of power, the tiny infinite threads of influence which make human communion so fascinating? If this were so, then I should be doing no service to Gary by dragging him into the criss-cross net of dissemblance and variegated moods which characterised most human contact. At least his deceit, his greed, his anger were bald and honest. What about his gratitude? This seemed more like a tentative fumbling into the sophisticated strings of half-truth. By showing me that he knew I expected gratitude Gary shone a torch of white clarity on the difference between my arcane confused values and the pristine directness of his own.

Such were my thoughts when I was summoned, not long afterwards, before a board of educational gurus whose purpose was to 'regularise' Gary's domestic circumstances and give official sanction to my role in his life. Either that or to remove him to a place of safety, I imagined. I went to the meeting in some trepidation, not relishing the idea of explaining myself to strangers. I need not have worried. The headmaster, Macpherson, was there, as was Phoebe Yorke. Mr Stonehouse had not been invited. The other two were a psychiatrist called Mrs Branfield, and an official woman in a duffel coat whose name I did not catch. Mrs Branfield was a surprise – elegant in a cashmere sweater and string of pearls, long luxuriant hair framing a pretty face. I would say she was no more than thirty. The duffel-coated woman was large and grubby, short straight hair turning to grey and a jacket under the coat from the breast pocket of which I could see half a dozen pencils, point uppermost, which had streaked the material with lead. They sat behind a long table, with myself opposite. Gary, of course, was not present. I decided not to tell him about the meeting until afterwards.

Macpherson led the discussion with a brief résumé of Gary's wayward career – his truancy, the loss of his mother, his volatility, the danger of his slipping into delinquency. 'I think we should all recognise', he said, 'that Gary Callinan has improved tremendously in the last months, since he has been in the rather unorthodox care of Mr Masters. Frankly, I would not have thought it possible in so short a time. There is no room for complacency. He still has a hard rock to climb, and his current co-operation is naturally fragile. I do suggest, however, that we encourage Mr Masters to continue, if only because the alternatives, all of them, cannot be good.'

Phoebe spoke next. She said I was the standard which Gary could see and strove to attain. The fact that he could not attain it should not intrude upon the decision of the board (it was the first time I realised that a 'decision' of some sort had to be made – I was being vetted!). The striving was all – it had value in itself because it enlarged Gary's experience and enabled him to find where he fitted. She was pleased that Gary liked beautiful things ('though perhaps that is only because they are his').

The duffel-coated woman then questioned me. 'Mr Masters,' she said heavily, 'you are, I believe, thirty-eight years old?'

'I am.'

'And Gary is fourteen. You are also unmarried.'

'Yes.'

'There is a lack of feminine influence in your household. At the moment.'

'If you mean that I have not contrived to abduct a mother for Gary, that is true.'

'There is no call for flippancy, Mr Masters. We are all trying to do the best for Gary, and we can only be guided by the evidence we have before us. It is of course important that we consider his moral welfare as well as his educational potential. Does it not strike you as odd that you should have, shall we say, taken this boy under your wing?'

'Not odd at all. Not nearly so odd as hearing his moral welfare chewed over by people who have not met him, to whom he is but a name on a file.'

'Please don't be angry, Mr Masters,' said Macpherson. 'It is, you know, a pretty weighty file. The boy has been brought to our notice many times in the past, long before he drifted into your care, and we do know much about him that,

71

perhaps, you don't. There was an occasion, over a year ago, when he was found selling pornographic magazines to other children outside the school gates. It was all we could do to prevent his appearing before a juvenile court.'

'I did not realise he had shown such initiative,' I said. The duffel-coat stared directly at me with naked hostility. 'You ask me here to allay your fears,' I went on, 'to reassure yourselves that you have not helplessly stood by while a boy whose interests you are obliged to protect, whether you are inclined to or not, has been dragged before your eyes into a nasty web of turpitude. You do not want to be accessories, to think that you may be blamed one day for condoning an unnatural and suspect arrangement. Well, I cannot dismiss those fears, though I may perhaps be able to dilute them. I shall not encourage Gary Callinan to sell dirty pictures in the street. It will eventually bore him anyway, and it is not a good idea to present commerce as being devoted to the movement of tedious ephemera. Far better he should sell something which engages his interest and makes him feel that enterprise is good and decent. As for my age and present bachelorhood, I like to think they are irrelevant, but in a very real sense of course they are not. Were there no homosexual element in my emotional furniture it is doubtful that I would have noticed the boy at all. I invite you to consider that you might be glad to acknowledge the unheralded benefits of the homophilic trait, which is generally either smothered to death by Christian guilt or distorted into a prurient obsession. No, Gary is not in danger. It would be unthinkable that his burden of memories should ever be added to in such a way. I was, and am, alive to his need for a parent, any kind of parent rather than the continued flopping around in a morass of anarchic freedom. Had I been married, with a clutch of growing children, I would not have been alive to that need, or would have blinked and forgotten it. In that sense, my being a thirty-eight-year-old unmarried

72

semi-employed writer is indeed relevant. There is space for Gary.'

This was no doubt a pompous speech. The duffel-coat clearly thought so, and scribbled throughout. She offered no rejoinder, however. The four huddled in conference for a minute or so. Macpherson then addressed me.

'How long do you think you can undertake this responsibility?'

'There cannot be any finite term to it,' I said. 'Gary must not be allowed to feel that he is on trial, that his present life is a treat which may be withdrawn at any time, a curse of limbo. I don't know what the future will bring, but having gone this far I must be ready for it. Stability will change him. The threat of being forsaken would reduce him to the status of a crumpled kitchen towel. Don't ask me to predict the outcome of all this. I did not plan it, did not seek it, there are times when I am heartily sick of it, but to send the boy back to his grandmother now would be cold cruelty of a ferocious kind.'

'May we make a suggestion? Gary will fit far more easily with you if he can see a piece of paper which states your relationship to him in clear terms. We would like you to consider becoming an official foster-parent to him. Unless that happens, he will remain in the limbo which you so graphically describe.'

The pretty psychiatrist then spoke for the first time. 'And it would also be useful if you would permit him to consult me whenever you feel the need, or he expresses a desire.'

'There is something I would like to do first,' I said. 'I should like to have the assent of his father.'

I spoke to Gary's father by telephone the next day, urging him to come to London. He said he could not, he was too busy, he had his family to consider. And in any case, what was it all about?

73

'You may remember when last we spoke you said you would spend some time with Gary. I still think that is important, and would do him the world of good, but I actually need to see you myself.'

'I don't have anything to say to you, Mr Masters. That sounds rude, I don't mean it to be. I mean, I'm not educated, I don't understand these things, I couldn't really talk to you. I only know my son is a curse and I won't have anything to do with him. If you think you can do something, go ahead. I won't stand in your way. Christ knows what you're really up to. You may be mad. For all I know you could be some sort of nutcase. It's not my concern, that's all I want you to know. It's nothing to do with me.'

'Legally, you are his parent and guardian. You are responsible for him.'

'Yeah, well that's as may be. But don't lumber me with problems. I've got enough on my plate.'

'Mr Callinan, the local authorities have asked me to be Gary's foster-father.'

'Well, well! Have they, now? Look, I'm sorry, Masters, you may think me a shit, I don't mind what you think. You may even be right. But I don't want to *know* anything. I don't want to be *asked* anything. I just want to be left out of it. Can't you see? Do me a favour!'

'I need your approval, not formally, but to satisfy myself. I cannot assume your responsibilities by decree – I must know you are in agreement.'

'Sure, sure, I agree. Go ahead, and don't bother me, that's all. I suppose you know what you're doing. If you're some kind of pervert, well, we all have to take what life chucks at us, don't we? Gary included!'

'That was unnecessary.'

'Sorry. You know what I mean. I'm in the dark, aren't I?'

'That's where you want to be, apparently.'

'Tell me, Masters. Is he all right? Is he behaving?'

74

'He's doing fine. I'll keep you posted. And thanks.'

'For what?'

'For not opposing me. And for being interested.'

I did not reveal the substance of the interview, still less the telephone conversation with Callinan, until two days later, when the letter arrived from the Borough Council, Social Services Division. Firm and factual, it read like a summons, but it gave Gary the proof that he needed:

Dear Mr Masters,

I am writing to confirm that you are now registered under the 1958 Children Act as a Private Foster-parent to Gary Callinan.

Yours sincerely,
Rose Ward (Social Worker)

I showed it to him over breakfast. He read it slowly and with difficulty, but sensing that it concerned him profoundly he persevered. 'What's this all about, then?' he asked, feigning nonchalance.

'It says I am to be your foster-parent, officially.'

'Yeah? Great! That means I can stay here for ever, right? This is my house, this is where I live. You can't turf me out!'

This was not quite the reaction I anticipated, but I concealed my surprise.

'Yes, it means something like that.'

'Can I go and tell my nan? Go on, it's Friday. No school tomorrow.'

'Yes, I think you should. And I've already told your father.'

'Him? What'yer tell *him* for. Ain't nothing to do with him.'

'I happen to think it is.'

'You happen . . . you always happen to think something or other. You think too much, Brian, that's your trouble. When's he coming?'

'He didn't say.'

'Good riddance. I'm here now. He can't touch me any more. This is *my* home, not his.'

I agreed that he should stay with his grandmother Friday night, and Saturday if he wanted, returning to Temple Grove Road on Sunday. After he left, I found a note from him. 'Dear Brian,' it said, 'I have taken one pound out of my spending money for tonight as you have got a pound left from last week's spends. I will give you a ring tonight. Lots love, Gary.'

Upstairs, next to the bathroom sink, there was another of his curious drawings, depicting once again two figures, the one taller than the other, both wearing what appeared to be high-neck sweaters. The mouth of the tall one was twisted and disfigured, he had a prominent Adam's apple, big eyes, big ears, and a small tuft of upstanding hair on the top of his head. The rest of the face was coloured in. The smaller figure had no hair, black holes for eyes, a straight mouth and another marked Adam's apple. Balloons issued from the figures. The tall one said, 'HELP ME. I HAVE A SORE FACE.' The smaller figure said, 'LOOK AT ME THEN. I AM BETTER THAN YOU.' I could not approach an understanding of the drawing's significance, though I had rarely seen anything which so positively shouted a need to be interpreted. What on earth was the 'sore face'? Utterly perplexing.

That evening, Gary telephoned from his grandmother's. 'I've told Nan all about it,' he said. 'Do you know what she said? She said how *long* was you gonna be my foster-father? Do you know what I told her? I said – until Brian flakes out.'

FOUR

SHOULD I HAVE known better? I anticipated that the tentative ordering of Gary's domestic life out of the shambles which had overwhelmed it previously would allow him to flourish and mature. Stability would bring its own reward, I imagined, and happiness visibly expand like yeast. It was not to be so simple.

Gary sought to earn points in a multitude of little ways, which were endearing not for their intrinsic value but for the motives and intentions behind them. He spent at least two hours cleaning the cooker until it shone as new, and was proud of his obvious achievement. More than that, he wanted me to be proud. When home from school, he made it his duty to answer the telephone and take useful, accurate messages (whose purport had none the less to be deciphered from eccentric spelling). Nothing was too much trouble. Eagerness, willingness informed his every action. At the same time, he behaved as a person secure in his surroundings, with those tiny hints of confidence which spatter the conduct of a man who belongs, who does not have to tread gingerly. Gary seemed to have grasped what he wanted, and would not easily let it escape his grip.

But the stealing continued, intensified, in parallel with the increased security. I gradually became aware that he was systematically and regularly deceiving, lying, with the sang-froid of a practised con man. Hardly a day went by without my suspecting him of something or other, yet so subtle was he that sometimes he contrived to arouse suspicion only to deflect it with injured and genuine innocence. Thus my tenuous trust was constantly placed in question, and as frequently restored with compound interest. It was a very clever game indeed, but who, in this shifting pattern of advantage, was playing with whom? The see-saw wobbled; who gave it the nudge?

There were times when I thought myself ridiculously and reprehensibly arrogant in presuming to have improved Gary's lot. Phoebe had said that a tremendous backlog of anger and hurt and confusion had made his inner world 'chaotic', but how could she know? And what if it was? Should it not be left alone, free of interfering prying fingers? If the boy's psyche was not private, what on earth was? I had no right to tamper, and no grounds to assume tampering was justified. As Helen had pointed out, I was exploiting Gary to serve intellectual curiosity and to titillate an adventure of the emotions. It was grotesque and vile in its selfishness. But how could I go back? Gary was dependent upon me for sustenance, for worth, for self-appraisal, for all those little bricks which together build a personality. It was perfectly obvious that his building collapsed from time to time, and that he had developed self-protecting measures to reconstruct it. He now looked to me to help in the reconstruction. I did not know what I was doing. The fact that I sometimes felt it was wrong even to try could not but hinder me. It was too late now. I had to go on. The pressure of uncertainty and doubt told on my nerves. While Gary was gaining in assurance, mine was dribbling away. It was as if he had to feed on my life-blood to replenish his. I was being emptied.

It was then that I imagined it was not I who was shamelessly using him to work theories on, but he who artfully manipulated me, just as the counsellor warned he would, to satisfy his demands in whichever way he chose to put them. Sometimes they were disguised, sometimes deceitful, sometimes guilelessly honest and raw. I was perpetually confused and increasingly apprehensive. I knew I was accepted as a surrogate parent if I were treated with the contempt generally visited upon a real one. I did not enjoy martyrdom; at least, I thought I didn't.

Then one day he took money from the small bank account which I had opened for him, without telling me. There was no ostensible use for it, and he would not reveal its intended purpose. I was angry; he responded with another huge outburst of furious screaming, like an animal at bay, telling me he was always trying to do his best and why was I so rotten to him? I said he must do a job for the next-door neighbour and hand the proceeds over to me to replace in his account. Gary was sullen, resentful, seething. He did the work with bad grace. I arranged with the neighbour to pay £5 in single pound notes, and he showed them to me beforehand. I surreptitiously made a note of the serial numbers before handing them back and asking him to pay Gary directly. The next day, when Gary gave me £5 with a grin of satisfaction and eyes asking for praise, I congratulated him and put the notes on my desk. Once alone, I examined them. They were not the notes received from the neighbour, which could only mean that he had a constant supply hidden somewhere and was using it as the need arose.

Two consequences issued from this depressing discovery. Grandmother Polly, whom her husband referred to as 'that beautiful long-nosed dimpled redhead' but whom I more and more perceived as a machiavellian schemer, was undermining me by passing Gary money in quantities I could only suspect. Why should it matter so much? Was I upset because efforts on his behalf were being subverted, or because they were *my* efforts? I was by no means sure, but felt myself oddly threatened.

79

It meant also that Gary was, perhaps irrevocably, tainted. He was without remorse, without even a moral dimension, motivated solely by the need for satiation. He was not so much self-centred, self-obsessed, as self-limited – he could understand nothing save that which gave him what he wanted and that which withheld it. He would adjust to the rules which I introduced, and value them only in so far as they served him. It was a game he was playing, after all, and I was the pawn. My heart beat faster as I pictured a bleak future, the amoral delinquent and his blind, complacent grandmother in collusion to shatter my equanimity in their unending greed to fill the boy's appalling void. It was melodramatic, no doubt, but I knew, by then, that it was possible. There was nothing that the woman would regard as unconscionable, nothing forbidden, if it gratified the grandson whose welfare she had so recklessly and stupidly abandoned. It was not I who was being undermined, but Gary. She would in her ignorance deny him every chance of resurrection. Thenceforth I began to consider her an invisible enemy, to be handled with delicate care, the one card in Gary's unwholesome pack which must somehow be rendered impotent.

Looking back, I now realise that is why I eventually insisted that Mr Callinan should drop everything and visit his son. There was a degree of selfishness in my urgency, for I secretly wanted his alliance, his availability if need should arise. He might have detected fear in my voice when I telephoned; I don't know. But he reluctantly agreed to meet me in the parking lot of a motorway restaurant.

I gave Gary only two hours' notice that I intended to bring his father to the house, mainly because I did not want him to work himself into a lather over it, and also to torpedo the possibility of his refusal. I need not have worried on that account. Gary was so excited by the prospect that he went around the house announcing to each empty room, 'My dad's coming! My dad's coming!', telling the dog, calling everyone he knew had a telephone, slapping the table. He washed his face several times, tidied his room until it competed with the penthouse at the Dorchester for spotlessness, prepared himself as for an audition. No, that is not quite right. It seemed to me that Gary wanted to show off to his father, to demonstrate how fortunate he was, and to show that he did not want anyone to feel compassion on his behalf. He was proud, and determined his father should notice he had reason to be. In a sense, he wanted above all to make clear that he did not *need* his father's attention any longer, that he could do quite well without, thank you. Mixed with this was, of course, the deep ineradicable and conflicting passion of belonging by blood to this man.

I recognised Callinan immediately, as he descended from the high driving-seat of his lorry, shirt-sleeves rolled up, hair thinning, ruddy outdoor complexion, a certain shyness, diffidence. We shook hands, and I said Gary was waiting to see him, if he had an hour or so to spare. He would follow me in my car, and would park his lorry at the end of the road. He was clearly nervous about the encounter. So, indeed, was I.

In the event, I left the two of them together at the kitchen table, ash-tray in the centre, facing each other in a kind of strained togetherness, like prisoners talking through glass. They did not embrace, or shake hands, but greeted each other across a porridge of impenetrable space. I went out to read the newspaper at a local café. I assumed Gary would make a coffee or something, and that they would both desire their conversation to be private. When I returned, Callinan had already left. Nothing dramatic had occurred, but Gary was in a perceptibly different mood, relaxed, relieved, unburdened. He did not want to talk about the visit, or even to mention his father. I formed the impression that, having been apprehensive at first, he had finally found it all rather boring, and was now anxious to get on with normal, real life. It was as if he had swept the debris of his paternity from his mind by this one experiment, and resolved his confusion. From that day, Gary was less regretful, less nostalgic. Mr Callinan disappeared from his life, and Gary never suggested he should repeat the visit.

Phoebe remained doggedly optimistic. Gary kept his regular twice-weekly appointments with her, and though he continued grinding pencils into the wall when potential failure loomed, he did not falter. 'His reading has improved enormously,' she told me, 'so if he doesn't give in, you shouldn't.' In a letter to me she was more precise. 'His commitment to reading is very tenuous. He does not show interest in stories, or finding out anything through the written word. He will not want to until he has mastered the mechanics of the operation. He is not ready for the phonetic struggles, but he is improving so rapidly the struggle may be less than he expects. He is showing signs of wanting to read, but makes obstacles for himself by his choices which are dauntingly difficult, usually rejecting the easier suggestions I proffer.'

Phoebe further opined that as Gary's confidence increased, so he faced an even greater threat, that of self-knowledge, of recognising his own depression and the self-destructive side of his character. He would have to learn a new way of being in the world, less dependent, less grasping, more productive, and the transition, so late in life (for such a short step towards maturity is usually made with emergence from infancy), was likely to be cataclysmic. This was not a prospect I relished.

After consultation with Macpherson, Phoebe and I agreed that Gary should visit the child psychiatrist, Mrs Branfield, once a week, for which purpose additional time off from school would be allowed. It was left to me, quite naturally, to broach the subject with him. I knew he would welcome another excuse to escape the competitive atmosphere of school, but he might well resent the inference of incompleteness.

I went to his room late one evening to switch off the relentless pop music and make my ritual connection before retiring with my book. The dog came with me and fixed upon me a brown-eyed gaze which defied me to banish him from the room. Gary's intuition was phenomenal. He knew that I was about to say something which would inflict yet another change on his constantly adapting world, and sought to deflect me immediately by the introduction of a different subject.

'You haven't forgotten my birthday, have you, Dad?' (This was also, with perfect timing, the first occasion on which he used this word with regard to me.)

'Of course I haven't. It's two weeks away.'

'Are you gonna let me have a day off school to celebrate, then?'

'People don't cancel life just because they have a birthday, you know.'

'Oh, go on, please, Dad. I'll help get everything ready, honest I will.'

'Look, Gary,' I said, 'if you use this as an excuse, then there'll be another excuse soon afterwards, and another. You don't really want me to say yes, anyway. We'll do something else for your birthday, something better than just playing truant.'

'Don't be daft,' he said. 'It won't be truant if you say so. They can't make me go if you say I'm not going, can they? It's what *you* say that counts, not them.' But he saw I was not going to be swayed, and pretended to be hurt, turning his face to the wall and pouting.

'We'll ask your nan to come round for the evening,' I said, 'and Phoebe, too. Do you want Phoebe to come?'

'Don't mind.'

'Well, that's settled, then. You might show a little more enthusiasm.'

'I told you once, I don't mind. Anyway, it's *my* birthday, so I should decide who's coming, shouldn't I?'

'If you like, yes. Who, then?'

Gary pondered for a bit. 'Mrs Hardcastle,' he said. 'I want Mrs Hardcastle to come. She's my friend.'

Considering his betrayal of her trust a couple of months before, I wondered how he could have forgotten, or why, if he hadn't, he should assume she would be willing to accept an invitation. The greater part of his thinking process was still an unfathomable mystery to me. (As it happened, he was right. She did come as soon as she was asked, and it was Gary himself who went round to issue the summons. In his deepest recesses he still clung on to his power to woo the world. Though he was gradually regarding himself as less than omnipotent, he still needed the assurance that he was forgivable.)

Gary was eager to prepare the meal, to turn it into an occasion of his making. In all the years he had spent with his grandmother, he had not buttered a slice of toast. That he was now anxious to give something in return was, I hoped, a sign of progress. So the plan was laid.

'Good night, then,' he said. 'I'm tired.' He wanted to be tucked in, another echo from infancy which in any other adolescent bursting into new shoes every few weeks would long since have become a ridiculous embarrassment.

'There's something I have to say to you first, Gary.'

'What's that?'

'I'm going to make arrangements for you to see someone else once a week.'

'Another teacher? What's wrong with Phoebe?'

'No, not another teacher. You're getting on all right with Phoebe. That's not what I mean.' I fumbled for the words and inevitably chose the wrong ones. 'I mean someone who's used to dealing with boys of your age, someone who can help you.'

'I don't need no help, not that sort. You mean a busybody. I know all about them sort of people.'

'They are qualified to sort out problems, that's all.'

'What problems have I got? You trying to make out I'm a loony or something?'

'No, Gary. You don't need to be a loony to have problems. All of us have some problem or another. There are many grown men, married with kids, who find it useful to talk to someone who's a stranger, someone who will listen and not ask questions. It's a bit like talking to a priest except that you don't get given a bag full of penance on your way out.'

'You mean a shrink . . . '

'I mean a psychiatrist, a person who's trained to understand.'

Gary suddenly laughed. 'Poor old Brian,' he said. 'You don't understand, so you want someone to help you, that's what it is. It's too much for you, isn't it? You want someone to hold your hand.'

I was not a little shaken, for he was right in a sense. He went on, 'You reckon that if you want to chuck it in you can turf me over to some quack who'll want to dose me up with pills and have me carted away to a loony-bin. You've got another think coming. They'll never do that to me. They wanted to take me mum away, but Nan wouldn't let them. She won't let them take me either.' Gary was now sitting up in the bed and looking at me defiantly.

'Steady on,' I said. 'You're going too fast. No one's talking about taking you away, and you can't really think I would encourage them to. There's no question of it, no suggestion even. I am only asking you to see this woman once a week, for a month or two, and if it doesn't work we'll scrap it.'

Gary's eyes softened, relaxed. Another conquest now promised, and he was always more adept at seducing the

85

attentions of a woman than of a man. His grandmother, Phoebe, Helen, Josie, I suppose they were all little bits of motherhood which he snatched at like a pauper offered bread. Suddenly I realised that I was the odd one out in this sequence. My position was false. I was not foster-father so much as pretend-mother, and the implications of such a grotesque relationship filled me with foreboding. These uncomfortable musings were interrupted by Gary himself. Not for the first time, it was *he* who appeared to save *me*.

'What's her name?'

'She's called Mrs Branfield. I think she might be French by birth. She's young and she's very nice.'

'All right then. Let's give it a whirl. When do I start?'

'I'll fix up an appointment for you the week after your birthday. You can take Monday afternoon off from school, I've already arranged that with your Headmaster, and when the summer holidays start you can work it out with her what day you will go.'

'That's if I last that long, mind. Don't forget I've got to have a holiday like everyone else.'

'OK. One bridge at a time. Now go to sleep, and don't worry. You might enjoy it.'

'I ain't worried. 'Night!' The dog, fed up with waiting, was now fast asleep at the foot of the bed. I turned out the light and went to my room, too tired for either Gibbon or Dick Francis, and went to sleep wondering what possible reason there could have been for that threat he remembered – to take his mother away. Had she been what her son called 'a loony'? Would anyone ever tell me? What on earth had I taken on?

Like everything else in this increasingly bizarre situation, Gary's birthday was an untamable mixture of spurious domestic normality and seemingly outrageous pretence. To make it still more complex, the attempt to simulate emotion clearly issued from the deepest sources.

Due to be present were Gary at the centre, Polly and her Norman, Stuart and Josie, Mrs Hardcastle, and myself. Gary had been in a state of nervous excitement all day, close to the tension one might expect when one's horse is favourite to win the Derby. He was ebullient, effervescent, jumpy and tense. He wanted above all to impress his grandmother with his ability to cope even when far from her stifling protection, yet keep that protection always in reserve for ultimate solace in calamity. It was a difficult trick to play, despite his native cunning, and he often found himself teetering on the brink of a swing in the wrong direction. It was interesting that he anticipated calamity in the midst of apparent success, as if he could not trust his world to turn in a regular manner but was always prepared for it to spiral helplessly off its axis. He was ever on the alert for disappointment, always dressed for despair. Today, however, he was high with the energy of happiness, dangerously close to full-blown incautious enjoyment.

Gary laid the table, prepared the fire, telephoned everyone again needlessly to make sure they were coming, and hovered by the front door waiting for arrivals. 'My nan likes a good fire,' he said. 'I'll look after it. I'll light it and keep it going. Leave it to me, OK?' Then, a few minutes later, 'Can I tell everyone where to sit?' This was not a day on which to deny him small satisfactions.

Polly had decked her fleshy body in a flowered summer frock and squeezed her feet into high-heeled shoes which threatened to snap beneath her weight. But it was her head which claimed attention. She had a flower in her hair, rouge on her cheeks, and bright lipstick applied with such abandon one would have thought she had never attempted to use the stuff before. Quite wrong, of course. Her style of make-up betokened a garish untutored youth which had not been conquered by subsequent experience. She was like a beached whale, stranded out of her time and milieu. Josie caught my attention for a brief second and raised her eyebrows in eloquent disbelief.

Norman, on the other hand, was sober in dress and conduct. He spoke little, only in response to a question, and oddly not once did he say a word to Gary. It was as though the boy had nothing to do with him, and he had no idea how to initiate any kind of relationship. There was certainly no connection of blood, this I knew, but he must have shared a home with Gary for years. From time to time he stretched his hand out to hold that of his wife, and they remained thus joined for minutes on end.

Josie and Stuart had concocted a scheme whereby Gary's various presents were concealed about the house, and the discovery of each one revealed a piece of paper which gave clues to the whereabouts of the next. He tore about the place irrepressibly, littering the floor with ripped-off wrapping paper and string which was severed with force. Polly bestirred herself with difficulty to clear up the mess as he went along, as one who knows her place and the duties life allocated to her. This completed, Gary sheepishly proffered me a gift, which quite took me aback. It was a desk-pen set in onyx and inscribed. Obviously his grandmother had colluded in the choice and the organisation, and just as obviously had footed the bill, but this did not concern me at the time. It was a curious insight into his ethical architecture that he should wish to make a gift to *anybody* on a day when he might normally expect to be the receiver. I reflected at the time, I remember, that never had I felt the smallest impulse to distribute bounty on my birthday, either in childhood or since. I could not make up my mind whether this was an attractive tradition within the family, which Gary had been used to, or an additional bribe felt by him obscurely (or by his grandmother with clarity) to be advisable to pin down an affection which might otherwise slide away. I was also not a little angry with myself for falling prey to such serpentine thoughts – I was learning to take nothing at its face value. Not until much later did I consider that he might well have merely wanted to say 'thank you' in the most delicate and least embarrassing manner possible.

That my so-called example might be having an effect upon him I was yet in no position to judge, despite the opinions of pedagogues. But it was perfectly clear that his presence had entangled my mental processes to the extent that I was less and less sure of my own judgment.

At one point during the evening, while Gary was transfixed with fascination by the fire, which he prodded with questionable necessity, I left him to chat with Josie and Stuart while I accompanied Norman to the garden. (Polly, replete with a variation of *bœuf bourguignon* into which Gary had tumbled everything he could lay his hands on, reclined lumpishly on the sofa and dozed.) I took the opportunity boldly to ask Norman how he and Polly had met.

'The dear thing used to run a boarding-house in Portsmouth. I went there once in search of bed and breakfast and stayed on.'

'Was it something like theatrical digs?'

'Not really. She had half a dozen rooms, and they were mostly occupied by residents, people who lived there all the time. It was a boarding-house, as I said.'

'What sort of people were they?'

'I never really knew. You know, I am not much of an enquirer. Perhaps you've noticed. I live and let live, don't ask questions, don't gossip, let people manage their lives as best they can and leave them in peace. Why do you want to know, anyway?'

'Just curious. I mean, it would help me to know more of Gary's background and antecedents.'

'I don't think it would, Mr Masters. [Norman was as formal

89

as he was reticent, formality affording him the distance which he considered his right. He was not a gossip because he did not want anyone to gossip about him.] All this was some years before Gary was born. Of course, Polly's daughter Grace was there, but that's all, apart from the lodgers.'

'And how old was she at the time?'

'Oh, I don't remember. Twelve, maybe fourteen. We came to London when Grace was sixteen, just after she met Gary's father. Not that he was the first, mind you.'

I sensed that Norman was reluctant to proceed with confidences. But I had to press him, or I would remain ignorant of the boy's initial emotional décor, of the influences which had formed him. 'Do you mean that she slept around?'

'Mr Masters, she was a very pretty girl. And very impressionable. She never found out how to deal with young men and was always treated badly by them. Poor Polly had to come to her rescue so many times. Grace was not a bad girl, just, well just foolhardy. You see, some of the lodgers at the house in Portsmouth had been pretty girls too. She had watched them being courted and flattered, and I suppose she came to the age when she wanted to copy them. Only natural, really.'

I was not sure how to express the suspicion I was beginning to entertain without offending this polite, decent, loyal, but obtuse man. Could he really be so naïve as not to appreciate the hints that were trickling from his reminiscence? Or had he known what was going on and preferred not to acknowledge it? Polly was, had for years been, the centre of his life. He could not allow himself to think she was anything less than an angel.

'Polly was marvellous,' he continued, 'a mother to them all. She gave them all her love, and they relied upon her. They wouldn't have known what to do without her, really. She cooked for them every evening, washed their clothes, looked after their visitors.'

'I wonder if Grace was a little jealous of them.'

'I don't think so. Grace was always Number One. And Polly had so much love to give, there was room for everyone.'

'Why did you all leave?'

Norman fidgeted, but would not answer. 'I think we'd better go back in, don't you? It must be time for me to take the good lady home.'

'Yes, of course,' I said. 'I don't want to keep you.' As I opened the back door for Norman to precede me, he stopped and held it closed. 'Please,' he said, 'don't ask Polly why she left. It was an unhappy time for her, and I wouldn't want her to be upset. That's all in the past now, and better forgotten. There was some trouble, you see, one of the girls let her down badly, and she thought it better in the circumstances to pack her bags and make a new life up here. I didn't want to influence her. She is a sensitive soul, and couldn't bear the betrayal. It hurt so much. She never did anyone any harm, you know. She wouldn't hurt a fly.'

'Don't worry,' I said. 'I shan't rake up old memories without cause. And, by the way, thank you.'

'It is I who should thank you,' he said. 'You've taken a weight off dear Polly's shoulders. She needs a rest.'

When we went back indoors, the party was in frantic disarray. Stuart had produced a bottle of whisky from somewhere, and Gary was in the process of wrenching it from his hands. I intervened, persuading Stuart not to resist but to let him take it. He was in the throes of some fierce crisis, and I didn't want it to flare into a conflagration. Polly, roused from her slumber by the commotion, was uttering little whimpering noises and rocking her head in her hands. Norman went straight to comfort her, grabbing her coat on the way. Stuart stood in dumbfounded misery, uncomprehending. Josie stared in acute apprehension, as if fearful of what would happen next. Mrs Hardcastle had left the room hastily and was fidgeting about upstairs, pretending to need the loo.

91

Meanwhile, Gary ran with the whisky into the kitchen and poured its contents down the sink before I could catch up with him. I am fairly certain that, if I had, I would not have prevented this, though I did raise my arm to hold his wrist before he could hurl the empty bottle to crash on to the floor. 'I'll get rid of that, Gary,' I said. 'Now go and say goodbye to your nan. I'll speak to you upstairs.'

He was already in bed, hiding his head beneath the sheets and shaking. I said nothing. It was he who spoke, a quiet muffled voice through the linen and blankets.

'Don't have any whisky here again, not if I'm here.'

'Why does it matter so much to you, Gary?' I asked.

'It killed my mum. I don't want it to kill you as well.'

'Thanks,' I said. 'But you should have told me, not taken the law into your own hands like that. What do you imagine people will think of you?'

'I don't give a fuck what they think. I *know*. They don't. That muck'll kill them. I don't ever want to see it again.'

'You'd better get some sleep,' I said, somewhat weakly. 'You've had a busy day.'

'Yeah. And I'm sorry it all got spoilt. Wasn't really my fault, though. 'Night.'

With a nightcap at the kitchen table, Josie, Stuart and I sat silently for a good five minutes. Then Josie spoke up. 'Stuart and I are taking a week off to have a break in the south of France,' she said. 'It'll be during the school holidays. Can we take Gary with us? Don't worry,' she said as I glanced towards Stuart. 'We've talked about it, and we both agree. It would do you a power of good, too.'

'By the way,' she added, 'I suppose you know what the trouble is. It's as clear as daylight. The daughter ran amok, did as she wanted to, got into the club, and the mother blamed everyone but herself. Young Gary was not expected or wanted, he was an embarrassment, a permanent reproof. To assuage her guilt, the daughter sought unending punishment. The little boy must have been contaminated by the atmosphere. God only knows what she had to endure, or, more to the point, what Gary had to witness.'

That Easter, the holiday duly took place, another new experience for the tyro foster-son, who had never been abroad, nor often, so far as I was able to make out, beyond the purlieus of suburban west London. He was predictably in a state of frenzied anticipation for days, and quite properly boasted to his friends in the street, with whom he now regularly spent a couple of hours 'up the caff', that he was going to have a 'real' holiday, by which he meant something more enticing than a day on the shingles at Herne Bay. I pondered what shifts in moral compensation would occur to a boy who had lied all his life, inventing causes for pride where there had been in reality only sources of shame, now that he did indeed have something worth boasting about − a holiday abroad with an actor and an actress, accepted as part of the company, almost a person among people, among adults. Would he cease to lie, now there was no need for lying? Or would the habit persist? Of course, it was not really a habit in that sense at all, but a deep moral imperative, an act of creative adjustment to a reality which tormented his self-esteem. Presumably, therefore, Gary would continue to invent and embellish, however much his reality might appear to improve, because such had become his route to the conquest of an unfriendly world. He would not so easily grow confident in his ability to impress merely because he had better grounds; there would remain the nagging fear that he would, on the contrary, be scorned. Telling lies was not a replacement activity, substituting one set of facts for another, but an essential strategy in the bid for survival. He could not do without them.

Nevertheless, I hoped that this succession of 'treats', often only barely yoked to desert, would gradually dismantle

93

Gary's enormous edifice of pretence. That was why I willingly acceded to Stuart's and Josie's proposition to take him to the south of France. It was, at least, worth a try. Besides, it would afford me some respite, time to take stock and make plans for the future. I knew that my responsibility could not now be abnegated, but I did not see ahead further than the end of the week, the resolution of the next crisis. What I would do if his failure at school became intolerable to him, if my instant pseudo-paternity offered no safe refuge, if, in short, his fragile assurance disintegrated before my eyes, I had not had time to consider.

Just how much these dimly perceived anxieties were silently silting up my brain became apparent when I went for a preliminary meeting with the psychiatrist, during Gary's absence in France, thinking that I would prepare her for what lay in store. As so often in these unscripted encounters, what emerged was less a résumé of Gary's needs than an embarrassing revelation of my own.

I cannot recall now exactly what I said. I told her that I trembled for Gary's well-being, that I could not envisage how he was to withstand disappointment if his grandmother continued to prop him up artificially and effectively prevent him from ever having to face it. She had always banished unhappiness from his path, or so she thought, so that he imagined happiness, or her sanitised version of it, was his due. My intercedence in his life threatened to scatter the bricks of his self-appraisal by forcing him to find his place in a world of cause and effect, of desert and reward, of transgression and punishment. Though I was not saddled with any religiosity which could poison him with notions of guilt or redemption through pain, still I had my own versions of 'sin' – deception, ingratitude, cruelty – which I probably expected him to take on wholesale. I could not offer him any other set of values but mine, because I could not be someone else. Did I have the right to impinge on another life in so ruthless a fashion? Was it not dreadful to attempt to undermine the fantasies and constructions of a young personality if all I had to put in their place were boring, dull, unimaginative rules of engagement to assist an ordinary passage through a dreary life with no end in view but to complete it with as little noise as possible? I remembered Peter Shaffer's disturbing play *Equus*, at the end of which the much-tried psychiatrist, played by Alec McCowen, agonised over his choice, whether to rob the horse-blinder of his passion and turn him into a quiescent law-abiding citizen, or to respect that passion as being *his* and risk exciting but destructive turmoil. I had been to the first night, when none in the audience knew what to expect, and that final scene, with the final spoken epilogue, had left me sobbing. With a shock, I realised that I was again close to sobbing now, that my voice was squeezed in my throat and my tears held back only by concentrated frowning.

'It obviously matters a great deal to you,' she said.

'Why should that boy have been dealt such a lousy hand?' I implored her for answers. She kept still. 'What on earth can be the justification for a life torpedoed at the start? To tell you the truth, the injustice of it sickens me. I don't see what chance he has if he has to fight an inheritance which he did not seek and cannot remove. He is carrying the faults and wickedness of others, and he is bound to do so all his life. He has no choice. Sometimes I think he is doomed, hopelessly and helplessly condemned to be punished for crimes committed before he was born. Where is the sense in that? The moral self-satisfaction of those who see the world as an ordered balance of right and wrong, in which one simply has to elect which way to go, makes me want to vomit. What priest would *dare* tell Gary he has only to choose the path of righteousness?'

'This is all very distressing to you.'

'I'm sorry. I don't usually behave like this before strangers.'

'That's not what I meant,' she said. 'But the emotion is there. You have to be doubly careful, both not to strain your

95

own resources and not to expect an alleviation of your distress through love of Gary. That would be still more unfair to him. Exactly what your relationship is to him must be crucial. He has got to see and feel that clearly, and not doubt its purpose or intention.'

'I would not make his memories more complex than they already are,' I said.

'Good. You don't mind my being frank, I know. Send him to me as soon as he gets home. I shall do what I can.'

The holiday in France, though marred by one mysterious incident, otherwise worked very well. I only know what Stuart and Josie told me, and they were fairly circumspect about it, probably because they wanted to give me the impression that I should rest easy in the knowledge that Gary could conduct himself reasonably, without provoking a fresh crisis at every turn. He had been jovial and relaxed, helpful when required and responsive to requests to fit in with their plans. He had not demanded their day should be organised to suit his wishes, as I had feared, but had been swimming, sailing, walking, and they always knew more or less where he was. If he had pinched anything from local shops he had been deft enough to escape detection. Perhaps he had not even tried.

Stuart and Josie remarked that he had in fact preferred to be with them and only rarely ventured out alone. He had given them cause to think he was nervous, scared of dealing with people unless he had the support and protection of his hosts. In their company, he had been chatty and congenial with others, holidaymakers and French residents, with whom they came into contact, ballooning with confidence and a sense of security. He avoided any circumstance which might expose him to coping by himself, and would feign to wimper and pout whenever it was suggested he make a sortie unescorted.

In this, once again, he was like an infant unwilling to allow adults out of his sight, recognisable in the bawling and shrieking child who tests every momentary abandonment. Yet this was a gangling and increasingly manly adolescent, who would normally be expected to place more, not less, distance between himself and those whom fate had decreed should look after him. The spirit of teenage independence, stubborn, venturesome, self-discovering and rebellious, had not yet touched him. He welcomed, even craved, that adult solicitude his contemporaries found irksome and restrictive.

One evening, as they all three sat eating a bouillabaisse on the veranda of the hotel, gossiping about the theatre and the Cannes Film Festival and watching the manicured mannequins who paraded up and down the street every evening in a seemingly interminably varied wardrobe, Gary had suddenly leant over and bitten Josie heavily on the upper arm. He had not drawn blood, but had left a mighty bruise, indicating a considerable amount of concentrated strength in the bite. Josie uttered a cry and stared at him in astonishment, so taken aback that she did not think to return the assault but rubbed her arm perplexedly. Gary immediately looked down at his plate, embarrassed at his own act, and said 'Sorry!' Stuart asked him to explain, but he merely sat in silent brooding, unwilling to elucidate, if indeed he could. Stuart sent him to bed, an order he did not resist.

The next day they decided not to refer to the incident, but to continue as if it had not occurred. They were anxious lest by coercing him into self-examination, by asking him to dredge into his subterranean thoughts, they might unleash a resentment that would frighten him with its power. Doubtless they were right at the time, but on his return I thought it behoved me to make some attempt to uncover this deep dark stream. One could not pretend to be blind for ever.

We were sitting in my study, me at my desk and Gary in the adjacent Victorian armchair. He told me the holiday was 'great' and that he had even spoken a few words of French. 'Wait till they hear about it at school,' he said. 'I bet none of them wankers've been to France. That'll make 'em sit up. You should see the bread, long sticks they are, you break them and cover the table with crumbs! No plates! The Frogs are backward, that's what they are.'

'Haven't you got something else to tell me?' I said.

'Like what?' He was almost sneering, challenging me to unhinge his peace.

'I think you do owe some kind of explanation for having given Josie such a shock.'

He visibly tensed, avoiding my gaze. 'Dunno what you're on about,' he said.

'Why did you bite her?'

He looked at the floor. 'She shouldn't have told you that,' he said, and I thought I detected a struggle to suppress some almighty wave surging up within him. I tried to inject a note of calm reason tinged with affection.

'Josie doesn't mean you any harm, you know that.'

'She didn't have to open her big mouth.'

'She wasn't telling tales, she was just mystified.'

The wave could no longer be contained. Gary's head sunk to his chest, he gripped the arms of the chair until his knuckles turned white. Alarmed, I moved towards him, stood in front of him and forced my hands under his, so that he was gripping me instead of the chair. The pressure did not relax. I saw that he was crying, not sobbing but unable to prevent his eyes from filling up. He did not look at me, but still gripping, and in a low, sinister, determined voice which I barely recognised, he said,

'Nobody says anything against my mum . . . NOBODY. I won't let them.'

I didn't expect this. 'Go on,' I said gently.

'She's dead. You can't talk about her.'

'But *you* can, if you want.'

98

'Why should I? She's mine. I'll keep her to myself. I cried for days afterwards, I don't mind telling you. I couldn't believe it, when she died. I just came home from school, and she died. If I hadn't gone to that fucking school, she might still be here. I could have helped her. No one else could, but I could. She relied on me. She knew I could help her. And I wasn't there. When I got home she was standing at the top of the stairs with a glass in her hand, drunk as usual. She told me to go and get her another bottle of Teacher's. I could see she didn't need it, shouldn't have any more. But I couldn't say so, could I? She was my mum. I went to the off-licence. When I came back she was lying at the bottom of the stairs, eyes open, dead. Her whisky was all over the wall.'

Gary paused, paralysed with terror as the memory stood stark and bright in front of him. I saw it too, felt its power and its pity, and was moved by such woeful useless compassion that I wanted to put my arms around him and shield him from the misery of recollection. But I didn't; it was, as he said, *his* memory; I had no part of it, no right to dilute its exclus-iveness. After a while, during which he seemed to struggle with a resolve to avenge, he went on.

'And you, you want me to go back to school all the time, you go *on* and *on* about school. What did it do for me? It took my mum away, that's what it did. It kept me away from her. And she died. I wanted to throw myself under a bus. I stood there on the pavement thinking about it, wondering if I'd see the driver's face as I went in front of him. No one would get me back to that fucking place, until *you* came along. I dunno what you expect. Just don't let anyone talk about her, that's all. Anyone who does, I'll kill him. I tell you, I'll *kill* him.'

Gary dried his eyes with the back of his hand, now released. His face was white, bleached and drained of blood. He suddenly seemed like an old man, who had suffered marriage, bereavement, grief, a lifetime of heavy sorrows, deprived of youth and of joy. I offered him my pocket handkerchief, but forbore to be more tactile. He waved the handkerchief away, simply saying, 'I'm going to bed.' And he walked out of the room.

I was left wondering what Josie could have said to trigger this reaction, dormant but unnerving in its destructive power. There was no point in asking her. It was more than likely an innocent remark, not even a direct enquiry, perhaps not even ostensibly relating to Gary's mother at all. How often does one unwittingly release a dam with a casually thrown pebble! Gary's dam must have felt like concrete to him, and he would one day have to allow it to be breached. How and when was the problem.

All my impulses urged indulgence, forgiveness, patience. On intellectual grounds, surely such virtues, I told myself, were more likely to induce beneficent results than harsh, punitive coldness, on the principle that the sun makes the cactus flower while the brutal wind only stiffens its needles? Yet I had to force myself to act against my own argument, for had I not seen the truly awful effects of Polly's squelching softness, never having once demanded anything of her grandson, enfolding him with a protective gooey love which so unfitted him for adulthood that he approached it with fear? After all, the cactus must have its needles strong as well as its blossom sweet.

Emotionally, too, I was predisposed to treat Gary with kindness, for who does not rejoice at a smile of unharassed contentment? Anybody who knew the boy would want to see him happy. Kindness can also be self-regarding, earning quick reward for little effort, and I was alive to the attraction of these easy honours. But this too I had perforce to resist, for nothing could be more harmful to him (and, in the end, to myself) than any suspicion that the bonds which held me to my task should be tethered by emotion. He had to be certain that my concern for his welfare and ultimate advancement was disinterested, unalloyed. Whether he *liked* me or not was a matter of no importance. I must be paternal, and guided only by the recognition of what was good for him. And in this I was still learning as I went along.

In my determination not to be weakly indulgent, therefore, I sometimes erred in the opposite direction, spotting dissemblance where I should have acknowledged truth.

One evening, we broke the rule which forbade outings on school-days to join a girlfriend of mine, receptionist at an hotel, to celebrate her birthday. We all three went to a small Italian restaurant, and Gary was permitted two or three glasses of wine, though he normally showed no sign of interest in alcohol. (Only beer, the passport to working-class *bonhomie*, held any allure.) The next morning Gary complained of feeling ill. I was quite convinced that this was mere play-acting, either an excuse to miss school, and one which on the face of it would seem to be quite reasonable, or a badge of entry to the adult world, indicating that he, too, might sometimes have 'one over the top' and would be made to suffer for it like any other man. I would brook no refusal. Of course he was all right, and he would go to school in the normal way! He put his school-tie on with more than customary reluctance, looked pale and self-pitying at breakfast, drank only half his cup of tea. I packed him off to the bus-stop.

Two hours later I received a telephone call from the school, informing me that Gary had been sick on the bus, had again vomited in the class-room, and was now repining in the medical room. Would I please come and fetch him? He ought to be in bed!

Back home, I put him to bed with a hot-water bottle, twice being summoned for a bowl when he wanted to throw up again, and he stayed there for four hours. Perhaps it had been mild food-poisoning rather than a couple of glasses of wine, but it certainly appeared genuine, and I reflected that not even Gary, with all his guile, could induce such a manifestation of illness. His pathetic lament was a kind of reproach. 'You can't say I was pretending,' he said.

As the weeks went by, I gradually came to recognise that the withdrawal of approval was finally my only lever of influence over Gary. I had known from the beginning that threats would be barren, and indeed had never been tempted to use them. They were not the kind of admonition which naturally suggested itself to me anyway, and if I once allowed myself to resort to those methods there would be no greater demonstration that the influence was in the other direction, that he would be effecting a change on me. But I additionally decided they would cause Gary to retreat, when what he most needed was to advance. Nor, as I have already said, did I much care for the notion of reward. If, on the other hand, he noticed that his behaviour had in some degree rendered me quieter than usual, he would ruminate and worry, his customary bombast for the moment restrained, and would look for ways to regain favour.

Presumably, parents discover the power of disapproval as part of the learning process when they and their offspring jockey for position *vis-à-vis* one another in the course of their adjustment to life together. A parent does not know these things by some ordained instinct but must pick them up through experience, often surprising, sometimes painful. But they begin to test their arrangements from infancy, and have many years to hone them before adolescence throws everything into a higher gear. I was having to telescope all those years into a few months, which is why I did not immediately intuit the obvious, and my learning process was made more tortuous by the fact that at times Gary wanted to be treated as an infant, at times as a young man.

Had I been practised as a parent, I would also have known that there is no shame or defeat when the child exerts influence over his father as well as being subject to it. No man can be the same after the event of fatherhood, and he must recognise that to keep the filial relationship in repair he will be required to make his character fit the new circumstances, and that this involves accepting change. Of course, my outward life had already been transformed by Gary's invasion, but I was wrong to worry lest my ways of thinking and responding should also undergo some shifts. I felt that I should somehow be wanting in responsibility if I failed to have a good influence upon him, that the whole burden of change lay upon me, and that should I be revealed as malleable or tractable I would not have been up to the job. In this I was wrong, as any parent could have told me, and in time I would be bound to acknowledge that Gary, or Gary's plight and the state of his personality, had possibly influenced me far more profoundly than my care had benefited him.

But that is to anticipate. There was one occasion in late spring when I discovered that a certain distance, or unwillingness to confide, also bore fine fruit. Gary was becoming used to sharing my life, knowing my intentions, hearing my views, especially as they affected him. It confirmed his belief that he mattered, because, far from being secretive or reticent, I talked about ordinary daily events at the house openly.

A French girl came briefly to occupy a spare room at the top. She was a friend of a friend, not someone I personally knew, and the idea was that she should stay with us while she looked for a more permanent abode in London. It soon became clear that she would not be an easy guest. She barged into the kitchen when she felt like it, not saying a word to anyone; she asked for locks to be fitted to her bedroom door (a request I firmly refused); she expected letters to be taken up to her, as though she were lodged in a very expensive hotel. Though I asked no money from her, I did after a few weeks suggest she should contribute to the telephone bill; she used it freely and frequently, and I proposed she should not only pay for her calls but also help towards the standing charge, as she benefited from the convenience of not having to go out to a kiosk in the street.

Her reply was devastating. She had added up the cost of her calls and intended to present me with this, and this alone, when she was ready. She saw no reason why she should pay any more, and I should not bother her on the matter any further. I said, in that case, she obviously did not fit in the household and she should find somewhere else to live forthwith. No, she said, she didn't think she would. She found herself comfortable here and intended to stay. So the idea of a temporary bolt-hole had been transformed into the settled conviction she had a permanent home.

This I simply could not countenance. Quite apart from the horror of having to shelter in my house a person whom I no longer chose to have there, the inevitability of tension arising in an atmosphere I ought to maintain as equable as possible for Gary's sake made it imperative I should get her out speedily. Our conversations on the matter, which became steadily more vicious as I accused her of polluting the house and she told me I was a rampant exploiter, all took place while Gary was at school. I told her frankly that I wanted above all to protect him from any awareness of this nauseating business.

I next received a call from a lawyer at the local Citizens' Advice Bureau, who told me the girl had consulted him and he felt obliged to point out to me that, whether she paid rent or not, she was protected by law and could not be summarily evicted. She was in fact a rent-free tenant, but a tenant nevertheless. I made it clear that I did not run a boarding-house, and she was henceforth a trespasser as far as I was concerned. He said that if I persisted in this attitude I would find myself arraigned before the courts.

A uniformed police officer called on me without warning.

Luckily, Gary had just left to catch his bus, otherwise I doubt whether I would have been able to persuade him to leave at all. To him, all policemen were 'bastards' and he would relish the excitement of being in conflict with 'the fuzz'. I simply could not permit him to witness a situation wherein I was on the wrong side of the law. The effect, I thought, would ruin our progress thus far.

The policeman was sympathetic. 'I don't make the law, sir,' he said, 'and I am not bound to say I agree with it. But I must explain it to you. You do not have the right to enter the young lady's room at any time. If you do, you can be accused of harassment, and if found guilty could be sentenced to a fine of six months' imprisonment.' This in spite of the fact that it was my room, stuffed with my furniture, that she sat on my chair to make herself up in front of my mirror and slept on a bed which belonged to me in sheets which I provided. The scenario was perverse, Kafkaesque.

'She, on the other hand,' the policeman continued, 'has the right to use the bathroom and kitchen here, and you must not prevent her.'

'I'll put locks on the kitchen door.'

'Then, sir, I shall be obliged to send an officer to remove them.' All the privileges were hers, none were mine.

I told the man how important it was that he should not call again, as I had a foster-son whose understanding of the policeman's role was not benign. It seemed that I could give her a month's notice, but she could appeal for an extension to six months, which would be granted automatically, after which time I might be able to remove her. I could not, and would not, wait so long.

The manner of her departure is not entirely relevant. I visited her employer and told him what a curse she had turned out to be, and I believe he threatened to dismiss her unless she relented. She was one of those awesome, deadly females, mercifully few, conscious of their 'rights' and determined at all costs to uphold them. Considerations of humanity or decency were lost on her, and I was sure she wanted to stay not because she liked the house, as she claimed (how could she, knowing by now that I detested her?), but from a spirit of vengeance.

She left quietly one Thursday afternoon, never to be seen again, and bearing, for all I know to this day, a corrosive grudge against me.

'I see you've got rid of the Frog,' said Gary that evening. I had striven hard to avoid his knowing that I wanted to 'get rid' of her.

'Yeah, I know,' he said. 'You kept it all from me, didn't you? Well, I'm not so stupid.'

'I didn't want you to be bothered with it,' I said lamely. 'It was my problem, not yours.'

'Do you think I didn't know what was on your mind? It was written all over your face. You should have told me. Maybe I could have helped. What are sons for?'

He sounded sane and reasonable, but I knew that my failure to confide in him had hurt him somewhat. I had made him feel like an outsider, a feeling he had carried with him for so long and wanted now to shake off. I resolved then that I would not place such distance between us if I could help it. Distance was one of his deepest fears.

'Now that room's empty,' he said, 'I'll clear it up. We can use it for something. By the time I've finished with it, you won't know she'd ever been there. Then you'll really be rid of her.'

He never did learn of the police officer's visit.

FIVE

IT WAS SEVERAL weeks after Gary's birthday that I discovered one of his typically laconic notes, scrawled on a page torn out of his exercise book and dropped like litter on his bedroom floor. These messages, usually enigmatic, were always intended to be seen. This one was plainer than the general run, quite without ambiguity, and probably not originally meant for my eyes at all.

The note had been written on his birthday. It occupied the whole page, was negligent of lines, and grew steadily more bold and furious, each word written larger than its predecessor. This is what he wrote:

Dear dad,
    Thankyou For youre presant it was the best I have ever had Like Shit. This is wought you are

Gary

I was stunned by this. The note must have been addressed to me, I thought, yet I could not comprehend its anger. Gary had seemed happy that day, had been surrounded by affection, of which he had many tangible proofs, and had bounced with vitality and fun. After a moment, however, I realised that the anger of the message must reveal its purpose; it was directed not at me but at Mr Callinan. Despite the gifts from his nan, from myself, from his new friends in the house, there had been one missing, from a man he barely knew, had seen only a matter of days in his whole life, and whom he professed to despise. There could hardly have been a more vivid expression of primitive need. He had clearly not sent the note, I supposed for fear that it would further alienate the man to whom he was tied by blood.

The day before, I had announced, as carefully as I could, that I would have to leave for a lecture tour in the United States, and that I would be away for six weeks. I had known of this commitment for some time, and had kept it from him longer, perhaps, than I ought, because I suspected that a prolonged absence would be felt by him as a new abandonment. I finally presented it to Gary as an adventure, a time of testing, when all the work we had put in together would reap the reward of his being able to continue in his endeavours without constant surveillance. He was now old enough and mature enough, I said, to carry on in my absence, get himself up in the morning, go to school, and maintain his contacts with Phoebe and with Mrs Branfield. Stuart or Josie, or both, would see that he had a meal in the evening, but he would have to manage his own breakfast, and he could visit his grandmother without having to seek permission all the time. I said I would rely on him to show how grown-up he had become.

Gary accepted all this with a display of robust calm. Of course he would be all right. He would show me how reliable he was. And he didn't need anyone else to look after him, either. He could get his own dinner ready if he wanted. It was his home, wasn't it? He didn't need other people to invite him to eat in his own house!

I welcomed this resolve. It was precisely what I wanted, for him to turn the necessity of my absence to advantage, even to interpret my putting him temporarily in charge of his own life as an indication of trust. Though I did not say so, I wanted

Gary to recognise in some way that his grandmother had never shown such confidence in him as to leave him to his own devices. Sooner or later he would have to learn self-reliance.

Then came the note on the floor, which even if not meant to be found none the less placed a weight on my conscience. It reminded me that, by going away, I could be just as bloody as his real father and just as selfish.

When the day came for my departure, Gary did two contradictory things which were each highly characteristic. Because I was leaving early in the morning, he left yet another note, this time definitely intended for me, to show that he was already in control:

Brian.
    I have put Coffey in the perkulater for to moroy morning. Wack me at 7:30.

                                    Lots love, your Son
                                              Gary

His other act was far less agreeable. It was not until I reached the airport that I noticed my cigarette lighter was missing. (Like Gary, I had lapsed and my consumption of cigarettes was increasing daily.) I had placed the lighter in my pocket, as was my habit, of that there could be no doubt. Obviously Gary had lifted it. I was angry, disappointed, perturbed, all at once. It was extraordinary how easily that boy could send my mind into a turmoil. Naturally one did not need to be a graduate in psychiatry to spot the mechanism at work – it was simply something of me which he wished to retain – but I was not disposed to feel generously about it at that moment. Gary was even cleverer than that. He knew the lighter, a solid gold Dunhill which had been given to me by a girlfriend years before, was something I prized highly, and by keeping this, rather than an object to which I might be indifferent, he would ensure my return. Further, because the lighter was precious to me, he would be afforded the opportunity to show how carefully he would look after it. It would assume the role of a symbol of mutual trust.

I telephoned from the airport and told him I was upset he should steal from me. Gary was hurt at my use of the word, and there was a pregnant pause as he fought with his normal urge to scream outraged innocence. 'Don't go on at me,' he said. 'It's safe with me. I promise.' He had learnt something substantial in those months, namely that a reprimand was not always an attack, and that an attack was not necessarily mortal.

Gary corresponded regularly with me while I was away. I had provided him with a list of addresses and prevailed upon him to find a map of the United States so that he might follow my itinerary, and absorb some geography by accident, as it were. The first letter announced that he had met a girl at the skating-rink and that they were 'going together'. She was called Audrey, a singularly doleful name for a teenager these days, I thought, but Gary seemed to equate her with Helen of Troy and to him the name she bore was no less alluring than Delilah.

It was significant that Audrey came upon the scene when I was usefully absent. Was this because he did not wish me to know her? Or did he in some obscure way want to make me jealous? I should add that there was never any indication that Gary could entertain thoughts of a homo-erotic nature. It was indeed something to be grateful for, that he was not sexually confused or experimental. The most he had ever done, very soon after he had moved in, was to proclaim the news that he already had 'lots of hairs', and this in a spirit of jolly boastfulness, not lewdness. Not once did he show any curiosity about maleness, except in so far as it enhanced his vision of his own potency. Thus, when I say that the advent of Audrey may have contained an element of guile in order to incite jealousy, I mean only that he may have wanted to demonstrate that he did not need me so much as I might have imagined, and that I could go off whenever I liked as far as he was concerned.

I was never to meet Audrey, as her brief star spluttered out even before my return from the US. But like a fretting parent I wondered how he would deal with the end of the affair. We had talked about girlfriends in principle, and I had tried to prepare him for the awful ache of rejection and contempt, if only because I held a very real fear that he might react in a way quite out of proportion to the offence, that he would not have the inner strength to recover from the experience. Feeling melodramatic (not for the first time), I envisaged Gary tearing at the face of a lover who spurned him, and to obviate such an outcome I had indulged in some discursive conversations on love and marriage. He did not question my own lack of knowledge; Heaven knows what he thought I had done with my time. On the rare occasions when a woman other than Helen stayed overnight, usually only because she had missed her tube and didn't want to pay for a cab, Gary smirked mischievously, and I preferred him to remain in error on this than to be disappointed by the banal truth. Yet he had never appeared to attach much importance to it, and did not see in it a cause for teasing. Nor did it corrupt him into a desire to emulate. On this subject, if on few others, he was astonishingly sensible.

Gary's first letter to me during my stay in America brought Audrey to the foreground, only to be eclipsed a few lines later by Dunhill:

Dear Brian,
    I hope you had a nice trip over to New York and don't for get London Rules Still. I am righting at 1 am my time and

7 pm yours. Audrey came round to nan's and nan and Norman like her. She sends her love and lots of luck on tuesday [the date of my first lecture]. I must go I am tryed [i.e. tired] (and taking GOOD CARE of your lighter) So Dont Whery.

Lots love,
Gary

The following letter appeared to have been written earlier, before Audrey's advent:

Dear Brian,

It seems strange now you are away. After you had gone to the airport I was looking to see if I could see you in your seat. The best thing about School on Monday was Mrs Ross made me do some algebra. I like algebra. The worst thing was the new art teacher is not as nice as Mrs Rosman. I am now at Nan's. We have looket up 5th ave on the map of New york it is a big place. I have done some spelling and reading. I do not wont eney more algbrar today. I go to Phoebe's early the Jackdor lets me strock him. I was going home on Wensday and I was asked to pay 35 p extar so I have to pay a pound return.

Lots love Gary

The information implying financial hardship concealed, I assumed, some guilt about theft or, more likely, a successful imprecation to Nan's infinite bounty, of which he knew I would disapprove. By the time the third letter arrived, Audrey had been and gone:

Dear Brian,

I am wrighting to tell you that I am now longer going out with Audrey. I am a bit up Seat [upset] But not as much as you said I wold be. I am still Behaving at School. Nan and

Norman are orright with me and well. hope to see you soon.

Lots love Gary

Phoebe kept me posted as well, and her letters confirmed the efforts Gary was making to be dependable. Here are two of them:

Dear Brian,

I'm sure you will be relieved to know that all arrangements seem to be working out with Gary. He arrives here early, and so do I. As he, I suspect, fancies himself as a man-about-town he does not bring school work, so it leaves me freer to teach what I want. He likes a book I encouraged him to read and tells me he is reading 'West Side Story' with the class at school — (seems to suit him as he is the only one who knows tunes to the songs!). When he wrote his letter he said, 'I really enjoyed doing that.' He talks a great deal about you. You are missed and he freely admits it. I spoke to his nan yesterday because she wondered if he could come once a week for three hours because of the high cost of fares! We sorted it out. I suggested he gets a return ticket and continues to come twice a week.

He works much harder here and with less resistance and is steadier. It could well be the novelty but, whatever it is, it has helped a great deal of work to be achieved this week. After he has finished I can let him have a few minutes of handiwork — so expect to be welcomed back with home-made presents. I am constantly reminding him gently to keep your lighter safely.

Sincerely,
Phoebe

How well I recognised the reference to Grandmother's intervention. Ever the manipulator, Gary had wanted to show that

113

he dictated what he would do according to his own lights, and would engage Nan to do his bidding. I was glad Phoebe had been alive to the strategy and had countered it. The odd thing was that he did not want to surrender visits to 'his' tutor, but wanted only that they should not take place in obedience to instructions. There was a hint in the next letter that Grandmother had not just encouraged this spirit but instigated it:

Gary's journey to me (or rather the continuance of his journeyings) is reminiscent of Bunyan's Pilgrims Progress! We've had Sloughs of Despond mixed up with feet bruised by a swing-door, and a great variety of daunting afflictions and drawbacks. However, through all these, the school and I have cheered Gary on and he is still coming and working amazingly well. He is far easier to teach now – he will soak up an amazing amount of education in a short time and be ready for the next dose. I prepare more than half an exercise book for each session. I wouldn't want you to think Gary is coming reluctantly with many excuses. He is just being slightly weakened with sympathy and he appreciates when I counter with the 'it won't kill you' type of rough strength. The amazing and encouraging thing is that he is coming.

I understand that he has been quiet for several weeks at school with one exception, which *he* dealt with responsibly after the initial outburst. I see more positive than negative in that incident. Now I think the school is ready to welcome you back with great relief. The letters are his own work written at home in his own time, without me breathing down his neck. (Maybe a glimpse of the generosity we wish for him?)

Yours sincerely,
Phoebe

My own letters to Gary are now acutely embarrassing to read, so I forbear to include them. I obviously did not know what

114

voice to use for a father writing to his son, so they appear arch and contrived. I chatted about electric typewriters, about New York, and about the latest pop music. I exhorted him to look up all the cities I was to visit and learn which states they were in. I told him to behave and give me reasons to be proud of his progress, and to find the new plimsolls he had strangely hidden in the attic, which I would replace with some American sneakers, but *only* if he found them. They were an awkward mixture of adult gossip, condescending banter, and half-hearted attempts to show authority. I even threw in a joke, of which I am now ashamed, suggesting that Fate might intervene to find me a wife in America. What earthly good I expected that shaft of jocular betrayal to bring I cannot know. Perhaps I wanted him to visualise two parents instead of one, which was precisely the kind of fantastical wishful-thinking I had striven to make him abandon.

A telephone call received in Charleston, South Carolina, alerted me to the breakdown I had half expected. Gary was thrown out of school and told not to return. Phoebe expanded:

You must have heard that Gary has been suspended from school. It was for rudeness to a teacher and is effective for a fortnight (and until you get back which is implied but not stated). The bravado about this turn of events soon dissolved into real sadness which seemed much healthier and very painful for Gary. 'Even Brian is not always perfect,' he said. 'I did try not to make a mistake.' He has been back to apologise and was listened to, but is not yet allowed back. The dividing line of contrition, really being sorry for the act, and being sorry for being exposed, is a difficult one to fathom. The suspension has given him a shock at least and he does take more responsibility for his actions than I have seen before. (He blames his nan a bit. She should ring up the pub, he says, and get the police to catch him drinking

115

under age!) Amazingly, I have been able to talk to him more openly without his defences being too obstructive. It must be very painful to start to take a little responsibility. I've pointed out to Gary that when he said to the teacher 'you try and make me', they did just that – he let them win. He was really shaken that this time he hadn't merely walked out: he had been put out – a salutary experience. 'They' had the upper hand.

Gary is fine here with me. He is working well and behaving excellently – how fortunate I am! He wrote a charming letter to Mrs Hardcastle last Friday. It was not as well written as usual as he was disturbed by the suspension, but he persevered through this and was pleased with the result.

There is less of a protective shell of bravado around Gary now – I hope he lets you see the vulnerable rather pathetic little boy. He has missed you a lot and I believe he has progressed in self-awareness which has taken a lot of courage – an attribute that has been denied him by circumstances.

Best wishes,
Phoebe

It was difficult for me to picture him as a 'little boy' any longer – he was taller and stronger in build than I was – but it was symptomatic of his tardy development in other ways that he should still excite such a response. I anticipated my return to England with a mixture of emotions. There had not been a day when I had not thought of him and hoped that he was coping with the removal of my influence, and I had studiously written those long and silly letters every other day in an attempt to demonstrate that the connection was not ephemeral. At the same time I was becoming progressively more alarmed at what I had taken on and more anxious whether I could see it through. Quite apart from the business of getting on with my own life, continuing my attentions to the book I was trying to write in the midst of this constant upheaval, I was worried lest I should fail him by an ill-judged reaction or an intimation that his welfare was not my only concern. Gary had apparently placed all his hopes in me – Phoebe's letters, while reassuring me on one level, disquieted me in that they made this much plain – and while his responsibility in facing his own problems was huge, so were mine in helping him solve them.

When I did return, a perceptible shift occurred. My private social life had practically to be abandoned. Less and less did I take him to visit my friends, more and more I involved myself in banal domestic life. My only privacy was in my study, where Marie Corelli gave me respite (and I wonder now whether my slightly waspish account of her life owed something to the pressures which assailed me at the time), but as soon as I emerged I was once more driven to think of dinner-time, and homework, and tucking in, and delivering Gary from himself.

Never mind. I had to admit to myself that I enjoyed being 'Dad', even accepted without much demur the nasty incursions the role imposed. There was a danger that I might begin to indulge (or had already indulged) in a fantasy of which Gary was the prop. But Gary was not a fantasy; he was very real indeed.

I prevailed upon the headmaster to write a formal letter re-admitting him to the fold. It was important he should be regarded as normal, ordinary. That he should so regard himself was the rock of Sisyphus against which I must continue to labour.

Before the summer break, Gary had one more hurdle to cross. The school held internal examinations for its own purposes, to enable teachers to monitor the progress of pupils and make some comment for the direction of parents in their annual report. They were not especially important exams, and in Gary's case could not possibly offer accurate guidance in so short a time, but I was worried about them. He was bound not to do well, having missed so much in accumulated years of neglect, and I felt his performance might affect his subsequent mood. In the event it was a watershed of a kind, for Gary went into the abyss cheerfully, as if he had somehow spirited from nowhere the maturity necessary to withstand disappointment. At any rate, he was able to pretend that he had acquired it, and that, in his volatile condition, was almost as good. A year later, it was quite a different story, but for the moment, Gary appeared indifferent to exams and made no great fuss about the poor results. *They* did not know the truth about his abilities, he seemed to imply, only *we* did, so *their* exams could not possibly matter.

After a while, I had to make a conscious effort to resume some semblance of life-before-Gary. I made a point of dining at the club at least once a week, leaving the boy to his own devices, if only to indicate my independence. I began to accept dinner invitations, to avoid being totally submerged by parenthood. I was also busy reviewing and researching. Yet the transformation in my life seemed irreversible. I could not adapt. Out to dinner, I continually fretted and wondered what mood would greet me when I got home. I do not mean that Gary was perpetually troublesome. More often than not I would return to find him already shut in his room asleep, or watching television and just about to retire, bestowing upon the domestic routine a veneer of normality. But I had by now become used to being prepared for the worst, and imagining that some turbulence always awaited me. Moreover, I could only work when Gary was at school, or with his grandmother, or on the street corners with his mates. When he was present in the house, even if silent and reposeful, his need for attention quivered unheard and unseen.

At night I would pace up and down, drinking far too many large whiskies and pondering an awkward, variable, volatile future. The ironies shrieked at me; I was taking whisky surreptitiously, in a darkened room, lest my ward should catch me out!

The nightmares began soon afterwards. There was one in which Gary burst into the house, breaking down the front door and threatening to evict whoever was occupying 'his' room. Another depicted him causing a furore at the local pub, as the result of which I was forbidden ever to go there again. Still a third took place in court, where I was accused of nameless sins carrying the ultimate scourge of ignominy, and Gary figured as a waif and stray whose welfare had been neglected, supposedly by me, though dreams are rarely so precise. I remember a scene in which a torrent of obscenities came splashing from his lips. Often the nightmare was an amalgam of all these elements, leaving me exhausted and listless; I sometimes felt my face had been robbed of features in the assault, that lines and brows and cheeks had all been swept away in the draining experience of a hostile vision.

Despite the confusion inherent in their nature and diffuse structure, dreams are not deceivers. They remould the flotsam and debris of thoughts hanging over from the day and re-present them in less intelligible form. It is not the subject of the dream that matters so much as its mood. The mood of my dreams, after America, was remorselessly pessimistic; in them, Gary was a figure who harboured against the world a fierce resentment which no amount of attention could dislodge, and I was the scapegoat, the one against whom vengeance was wreaked. My nocturnal cud-chewing confirmed that I was beginning to see myself not as a saviour but a martyr.

This was a severe and dangerous development, not least

because it presaged a degree of egotism which made me seem, in my own eyes, a hypocrite. How could I honestly undertake to help Gary if my deepest concern was my own survival? If my energies were bent on saving my own skin, how could there be enough left over to devote to the saving of Gary's? This would be the deadliest betrayal, like beckoning a distrustful animal to one's side, then kicking it in the stomach. I had perforce to fight against such self-centredness. Worse, it suggested, as some of my friends had intimated already, that my desire to intercede with Fate on Gary's behalf disguised a more fundamental, barely perceived desire to assign to myself the role of one of life's victims. If this were true, then the whole enterprise was a charade, and I was using the boy's plight to construct and feed a view of myself which consciously I rejected but unconsciously might be the central core of my psyche. Gary would simply be the tool I had used to fashion a self-image which I could not do without.

These doubts, which I naturally kept to myself, increased with the weeks and months as Gary went through a fourth term at school. At least I could resist these moral and ethical dangers as long as I discerned their existence, comforting myself in the knowledge that much irrevocable harm is done to people from the purest ignorance, and that I stood less chance of doing wrong while I was aware how wrong could be done. The fact that he was now an attender at school, with the occasional truancy, was in itself an achievement.

Girlfriends followed one another in rapid sequence. He did not wish to bring them home to introduce them to me. Was he ashamed of our unusual arrangement? I would not have blamed him if he was, though he had given every indication that he was on the contrary proud. I might have been difficult to explain, and the girl's previous escorts must surely have been able to produce mother, father and siblings, not an unrelated foster-father in a house peopled with theatricals. No wonder Gary avoided awkward confrontations.

120

One girl seemed more likely to endure than the others. Gary spoke of her as being 'quiet', evidently a quality which betokened seriousness. He would talk to me about the dress he imagined she might be wearing that day, where she might be and what she might be saying. The wish to conjure her presence with talk, to create her by speaking her name and feeling the vibrations in the air as the dear syllables filled the room, was touching to behold. Pessimistic as I had become, I wondered what would shatter the bliss and how I would face the task of repair.

It was a Thursday in October when Gary's fragile control collapsed. A telephone call from the school told me that he had picked a fight with another boy who had made some reference to his (Gary's) girlfriend, which he had erroneously interpreted as a slight, and the ensuing scuffle had developed into a furious assault; a crowd had gathered round, urging the defendant on and chastising Gary for his intemperance, which served only to enrage him further. He threatened all and sundry, announcing that he would 'knife' anyone who got in his way, until a teacher intervened, and Gary set upon him. Two more teachers came to the aid of their colleague, eventually subduing Gary by sitting on him. The fact that it had taken three men to bring the boy, wild with anger, under control, both frightened them and insulted their sense of decorum. They had responded, stupidly I thought, by throwing at him the threat that he could be sent to prison for assault and that there were plenty of witnesses to his offence. Fortunately the Headmaster resisted the teachers' demands that he summon the police, and he called me instead.

I drove to the school immediately and found Gary sitting sullenly in the headmaster's office, cocky with spurious assurance and still fidgety. He stood up as soon as I entered. 'Let's get out of this place,' he said.

'You must ask Mr Macpherson's permission to leave,' I suggested.

'Sod him!' Normally, when Gary was beside himself, he retained a sufficient degree of embarrassment to look at the floor or at his clasped hands, as if disowning the demon which rose within him to manage his acts and speak with his voice. This time, he looked me straight in the eye as he said these words, defying me to show the anger which would confirm that I was on *their* side, against him. It would serve little purpose to gratify his need for battle-lines to be drawn in this way, and I knew well enough that if I declared my allegiance and rushed to his support he would want instant retribution, whereas if I withheld the support he would feel isolated and even more like a stag at bay. I turned to Macpherson. The last thing I should do at that point was apologise for Gary's behaviour.

'I'll come in with him tomorrow, if I may,' I said.

'We'd rather you didn't,' said the head. That 'we' was pregnant with significance. Gary had so intimidated these men that Macpherson sought protection in the plural. Had he said 'I' he would have been ranging himself alone against Gary, one to one. The inference of numbers gave him an authority he should have been able to muster without them. But I could not be surprised. I wondered at the boy's power, not strength but power of personal projection.

'We don't think it a good idea to see Gary tomorrow; he should take the day off to recover.' Gary, by this time, had already opened the door, without leave, and was walking down the corridor in what looked like a gesture of contemptuous independence, but was, I thought, fear of being discussed, pinned down, examined. He usually enjoyed being the object of interest and positively encouraged people to talk about him, but now he had seen the demon, and he did not want it to be brought into the open. He was afraid of its being acknowledged or understood, lest it thereby be made to cling to him, an ineradicable lesion on his character. This was something he must keep to himself; no one should be allowed

122

to make it common property by chat. He absolutely knew the danger lay in recognition.

'You do not intend to inform the police,' I said.

'No, Mr Masters. We are happy to leave the matter in your hands. But we should look for an assurance from you that such an incident will not be repeated before we admit him here again.'

'You know better than that,' I said. 'Every man is the sum of his acts, and every child is busy creating himself by those acts. They are autonomous, they are free, and they are unpredictable.'

'Existentialist, you mean?'

'If you like. But we don't require labels for what we both know to be true. The most I can promise you is that I shall do my best to make Gary see his conduct with my eyes, and perhaps yours, as well as his own. But, this done, he must return here on Monday. Let anyone loose in the world and there will be risk. Your school cannot be guaranteed exemption from it. It would also help if you were able to use Gary's eyes.'

'I do, Mr Masters, believe me I do. Gary shares his space with other people, however, and I have to see through their eyes as well. Please telephone me when you see the way clear.'

'Thank you.'

Gary was sitting in the car and smoking. (He had given up the pretence of being a totally reformed smoker, but rarely lit up in my presence.) We drove home more or less in silence. The only information he offered was, 'It wasn't my fault, you know.'

'You can tell me later,' I said. 'Just try to calm down.'

We spent the rest of that Thursday and the whole of Friday talking. It was an extraordinary experience, for it took an hour or two for his demeanour to shed its pitiful aggression, and I was by no means sure that it would. My words, my attitude, could unleash another explosion, or they could offer the assurance of togetherness and so defuse it. I could not be an accessory, but I had on the other hand to drop everything and concentrate attention on the exorcising of that demon. Gary had to feel that he would not be required, never be required as long as he was my responsibility, to face the evil alone.

I spoke very frankly to him. He admitted that his initial belligerence arose from the certainty that I was going to tear him off a strip, 'have a go' at him, as he put it. I told him there was no advantage in that, and asked him to relate exactly what had happened, as repetitiously as he liked. I then explained that his problem was fragility, that he was so terrified of losing anything once he had it that he imagined everyone was his enemy, about to rob him. That someone else should so much as mention his girlfriend was to take her from him, just as anyone who dared refer to his mother was undermining a precious personal memory. It was a form of jealousy.

'You get jealous too, it's not only me.'

'Sure I do. We are all subject to jealousy. We don't all express our frustrations in such a violent manner, though. We learn to hold them and wait until they are diluted.'

'You lose your temper sometimes.'

'Yes, I lose my temper from time to time. But I retain some measure of control. And so must you. It sounds boring, I know. You need to express yourself, and your means of expression, sometimes, is excessive. You can hurt people just by being yourself. You will enjoy people more when you know that their happiness depends upon your treatment of them. You will gain from control, not lose.'

'What about them, then. They can hurt me too.'

'Yes, I know. And I'm not going to tell you to turn the other cheek. Just think that they are frightened as well, and they might also need someone to be with them. No one can be alone. It's not just you. Everyone. You are not unique.'

A year earlier, Gary would not have listened. My strictures would have seemed incomprehensible to him, pious and foreign. Now, he was more in touch with himself, more willing to understand.

'You know something,' he said. 'I wish you'd met my mum. You'd have liked her. I bet you two would have got on.'

He went back to school the following Monday. A couple of months later, however, there occurred the threat of another deprivation, and one which no words of mine could alleviate, explain, or even define.

I have already told how, about twelve months earlier, Gary had to receive a tetanus injection, the prospect of which filled him with such horror that he could only be persuaded to endure it if I were present. He clung grimly to me all the while, eyes desperate with unnameable anxiety. The very idea of a hospital he had irrevocably rejected, and so the jab had been administered by my friendly neighbourhood doctor. I am quite convinced that had I or anyone else attempted to force Gary through the doors of a hospital we would have met with much more wild, ungovernable violence than anything the schoolmasters had witnessed. Hospitals were clearly a source of terror to him, and as the months went by I could only surmise that they had been associated in his experience with departure and death; I knew that Polly had frequently been ill, with one kidney and invincible obesity, and wondered, but avoided asking, if Grace's alcoholism had brought her often to a hospital bed. Hospitals were certainly inimical.

Just before Christmas, Polly announced grave news. Her beloved Norman had complained of stomach pains, and was now undergoing extensive examination at the West London Hospital. She feared the worst, but could not bring herself to name it. Would I go over and see her?

No sooner had Gary left for school than I motored over to those dismal flats. Polly sobbed into an absurdly tiny and pretty handkerchief as she took refuge in nostalgia and told me how she had been a bed-and-breakfast landlady when she had met Norman, how she was only good at one thing in life, and that was to look after people. She was happy cleaning shirts and cooking meals, and if there were no longer any shirts to clean or any meals to cook she would not want to live any more. She had no family apart from Norman, no children apart from her dead daughter, no grandchildren apart from Gary, whose future was now secure (she said) with me. If anything happened to Norman, she would kill herself. There would be no point in going on.

I could see she would be bereft if Norman suddenly, brutally, was taken from her, and I felt more warmly towards her than I had until then. Despair, misery, isolation may excite compassion even for a murderer, and, whatever I thought of Polly's disastrous theft of her grandson's self-confidence, I pitied her present vulnerability. She was, at root, an innocent, a rough, unlettered provincial lass who sinned by default. She was without real malice, and now she was being slowly sapped by emotional scouring. In her grey-ish flat, imbued with the smell of boiled food, she pined for the company of her man, inoffensive obedient Norman, the person she could cater for. She ate from an interminable plate of sandwiches, and waited all day for the telephone to ring.

When it did ring, it did not tell her what she wanted to hear. The doctors would need to speak with her. The news was not good. She should brace herself. Should they send an ambulance to fetch her? No, Mr Masters would accompany her to the hospital, she would be all right.

Polly wept or sniffled all the way to Hammersmith, and when she saw Norman, with majestic self-command, she beamed a broad grin at him, kissed him, and spread his bed with the goodies she had prepared – cakes, tarts, biscuits,

126

and some very special chocolates she had bought. The nurse, who scurried busily in and out (Norman had been provided with a small room to himself), frowned and wagged her finger at the sight of such booty. 'I don't know if you can manage all that, Norman,' she said, condescendingly. 'It's not *exactly* what the doctor had in mind for you.'

'You mind your own business, young lady,' said Polly. '*I'll* decide what to give my husband, not you, and I'll thank you to hold your tongue while I'm here. Your job is to keep things clean and do what the doctor tells you, not to meddle. Understand?'

I admired her pluck. The nurse was about to defend herself, but I managed to convey a message by a brief tug at her skirt, and she left. We left shortly afterwards, to talk to the doctor in charge.

Norman had a galloping cancer. The diagnosis stated that it was extensive and inoperable, having invaded the intestine, the bowel and the stomach. Were they to attempt to remove it, he would die on the table. The most they would attempt was to by-pass the intestine and construct a false anus in his side, leaving the cancer to do its work in the dark. He might not live more than a few months, perhaps less. He could go within weeks.

'Promise you won't tell Norman,' said Polly.

'That is entirely your decision, Mrs Galway,' said the doctor, an unsmiling man, but gentle in manner. 'If I might advise, however, I think it would be proper to tell your husband something of his condition; he is bound to consent to the operation, and there would be little point in disguising its purpose. You need not, on the other hand, give any notion of a time-limit. I hope you don't mind. We are more used to this kind of thing here than you might be. And I am terribly sorry to have to give you such sad tidings.'

'He never did anything to harm a soul. Why him? Why Norman?'

'Why is a question doctors never ask. Otherwise we would spend our time hurling insults at the sky or waving our fists at God, instead of trying to help people be more comfortable with their afflictions. Like you, we would despair for the lack of an answer.'

Polly thanked him, and heaved her mighty frame back into the room to sit with her husband. I left them alone there while the doctor and I exchanged necessary information. Norman then asked for a word with me.

'Do you know what she told me?' he said. 'She said this is the first time in all our married life that I have been able to have a little bit on the side.' He tried to laugh, but the smile turned to a grimace as the pain smote him. 'One day', he said, 'I'll tell you what happened to Grace. But let me get out of here first.'

From that day, throughout Norman's illness, I was almost as much the guardian and companion of Gary's grandmother as I was the warden of Gary's reconstruction. It was not easy to imagine the horror of Polly's position. I could not turn my mind to it. On the other hand, I had to envisage what would be the effect upon Gary. Another desertion, another departure, another removal of one of the stitches which had held his life together. Who could blame him if he ranted with impotent rage and surrendered the attempt to fit in with a world which turned all its guns against him? He would feel sorrow for his nan's sake, but would he want to help her? Or would he try to distance himself from grief? How much strength did he in fact possess? More even than this, and here I had to admit I wondered about my own fate, how much longer would he rely upon me when the time came that only one person was left of the dramatis personae of his infancy, and that one person felled by wretchedness? Was I, too, about to be left alone?

*

Norman did not last three months. He was sent home to die, and spent the last weeks drifting in and out of a feeble consciousness. I could not, dare not, ask him to expand his inconclusive remark about Grace. I told Gary he was seriously ill and prepared him for the end. He did not explode. He brooded, grappling in silence with the inconceivable. Polly Galway telephoned me late one night, after everyone had gone to bed.

'I've lost him,' she said. 'I've lost my Norman.'

'I'll be right over.'

Hurriedly pushing jeans over my pyjamas, I drove in the dark through empty streets to the flat, itself pervaded by emptiness. The front door did not, for once, hold something in or keep something out, but gently admitted the quiet gloom of the night. The lifeless air of London filtered through those walls, where Polly sat in an armchair, her gaze fixed upon the inert body lying on the sofa opposite.

'He just went,' she said. 'I gave him a cup of tea, and he went. Look, the tea's still there, on the floor where I left it for him.'

She would not sleep, but sat up all night. I lay on the floor and tried to doze, opening my eyes occasionally to be confronted by the profile, turned to the ceiling, of the dead man's face, and the other profile of a dumb woman, looking with unconquerable love and sadness upon the evaporation of her life.

Gary did not attend the funeral. 'Gives me the creeps,' he said. Norman was burnt to the sound of taped organ music. That evening, Gary said, 'I wonder who'll be next. There'll be someone, you wait and see. There's a jinx on me. I've told you before. You wait and see.'

Phoebe's Easter report on Gary's progress was again encouraging, though I had reluctantly to acknowledge, later, that the

Gary she saw was not quite the same person as the one I knew, still less the one who daily exercised his recalcitrant personality at school. It seemed he was endlessly manipulative, and showed whichever face was likely to turn events most favourably to his advantage, swapping masks to suit the strengths or weaknesses of his interlocutor. He was swift to size people up, accurate in his assessments, immediate in the application of them to variations in his conduct. Like a seasoned actor, he assumed and discarded character at will. There was nothing terribly wrong or unusual in this; we all do it to some extent or another. But it was unnerving in one so young, and it was overlain with that residual infantile desire to get whatever he wanted, however he wanted it. In many ways Gary was still in his cot, testing, stirring, drawing conclusions, learning how to get his little victories, and learning in particular that his strategy had to be adaptable.

Hence, that his tutor and his school responded differently towards him held no real surprises. Phoebe was positive, interpreting every sign in its best possible light and tempering her exuberance only with that insidious, unavoidable cynicism which attends every attempt to impart knowledge where it has not been sought. 'Gary', she wrote, 'has now almost passed the stage of having to learn to read.' Unfortunately, his ability to read was not accompanied by sufficient curiosity to enjoy what reading could offer. He was still not ready to recognise points of view or attitudes which were not his own. So, reading was a means to self-aggrandisement, a skill which was its own end.

'Gary has shown himself to have a good intellect and is beginning to learn to use it,' she continued. 'Perhaps the next stage is to learn to appreciate it. He is easily discouraged by the slightest failure, mistake or criticism. This is understandable but he must try to remember that a mistake does not cancel all the progress he has made and prove him foolish.'

She concluded with an exhortation directly addressed to

him (she knew well enough that he would want to see the report and I would accede to his request): 'Learn by your mistakes, Gary; do not let them take your confidence away.'

The boy beamed, raised his eyebrows, scratched his head, jumped up, sat down again, as if his skin could not contain the energy and enthusiasm which wanted to burst forth and fill the room. 'That's great, innit? You'll get a good report on me from school, too. I've been behaving meself.'

Did he really believe that? There must be a sense in which he *knew* he was not liked or appreciated at school, and that he had done precious little to earn praise or even tolerance. Since school did not matter to him, he must have felt that it would not matter in the general scheme of things, and that any pejorative opinion that might issue from that quarter could be dismissed. Gary could only respond to one person at a time; and he would then have undivided attention which he would grasp greedily for himself. To share a classroom, and take his little bit of attention while others took theirs, was simply impossible for him. He would prefer that 'others' did not exist, were not there, did not intrude. He was still hopelessly selfish.

Some of the written remarks of teachers were brutally straightforward. 'Gary only attends one lesson out of three. He usually arrives late, never brings his books, and rarely does any work once he has settled. He is wasting his time.' That was for French. In religious studies he was 'surly and belligerent', in science 'unreasonable and aggressive'. The metalwork teacher recognised the same problem as Phoebe: 'Gary gave up when he met a difficulty, but with sustained effort could have been quite good.'

There were two bright spots. In mathematics he was credited with 'some good work, which is extremely neat and very well presented'. There was an ominous added comment: 'If Gary worked as hard in class as he appears to work at home, he would make more progress.' In other words, he could only achieve if there was the promise of instant gratification, a word or a smile or a pat on the back, and since no such *uniquely* personal gift was within the power of the teacher there was no point in striving for it. Yet again, doing well was a means of earning the approbation of those one loved; since Gary was indifferent to the teachers at school, not caring whether they loved him or not, he would not put himself out to earn something he did not want. It must have appeared very simple to him. They were not worth bothering about. They took up valuable time. They did not exist. The subjects they taught did not matter. Mathematics was the one exception because he was able to carry it over from home (or from Phoebe's) and etch out, in that alien environment, some illustration of the security he felt he now had, almost by way of defiance.

Art was another exception. 'From a rather hesitant beginning Gary became excited by learning new techniques and ideas and this in turn generated a variety of interesting and unusual pieces of work.' I supposed that both mathematics and art were expressions of draughtsmanship, and each in its way mirrored a feeling of security – straight lines, perfectly-contained right-angles, controlled curves, and so on – whereas subjects which depended more on received knowledge than self-expression must have appeared amorphous and ambiguous, ungraspable because they did not enable Gary to extend *himself* – they were more like attacks which threatened to *change* him. Still, I should leave this to the psychiatrist, I thought. It was odd how I questioned and examined aspects of behaviour that, two years earlier, I would have allowed to pass unnoticed.

The Headmaster's summing-up was accurate, but not very helpful. 'While he shows some signs of maturity he is far too self-centred to join in any activity on equal terms.' A bull's-eye, that. 'I suspect that his liking for attention is a reason for his frequent unreasonable behaviour.' Yes, very perceptive,

except that behaviour cannot be properly deemed unreasonable once you have found a reason for it.

'You've done pretty well,' I told Gary. 'After several years
of truancy and hardly any schooling at all, I'd be a real fool to
expect any more, and I don't. What you have done doesn't
seem to satisfy some of these teachers, but I know what it has
taken for you to get this far. They don't realise that you have
scaled mountains to come to the foot of their hillock.'

'Yeah, well,' he said. 'I'm not sure what you're on about,
but it's OK, right?'

'Right.'

'We've got the exams next. I didn't tell you about them.
Shall I do them?'

'Of course you must take them.'

'It's just that, I thought, after these reports, they wouldn't
really be necessary, would they? Like we could skip 'em.'

'No way, Gary.'

'But I get so nervous. I'll be all of a sweat.'

'So will most of the others. And so am I when I have to give
a speech to a bunch of Tory ladies with hats on, or do a live
radio broadcast. That doesn't stop me doing it.'

'Come on, Dad. Don't be a bastard.'

'You will do the exams, and you will soon find that it's not
so big a deal.'

Gary's demeanour changed abruptly, as if he had been
insulted. 'I know that,' he said. 'You don't have to tell me. I
wasn't born yesterday. I've done exams before, right?'

So that was settled. What I did not confess was my worry
that the reports from individual teachers indicated, still, a
great deal of absenteeism. What was he doing when he was
not in class? Where could he be? There was only one accept-
able answer. I could quite understand that he would want to
spend more time with his grandmother since her bereavement, even that she would ask him to do so, without his
initiative. But the reports suggested that sporadic truancy had

133

been going on all year, since long before Norman's death. He must have simply got up and walked out of the school when he felt like it, gone to his grandmother's flat, and been received without a single hint of reprimand. Not once, but time and time again. Regularly. The collusion had gone on all year, probably for nearly two years, and in the meantime the hopes for Gary's future, concern at his difficulties, pain at his failings and hurt at his treachery had all been borne by me and people I had unwittingly roped in to this little circus revolving around him. Polly Galway had all the time been totally negative and obstructive. She simply couldn't give a damn, because she understood nothing.

SIX

Gary's second round of examinations came at the end of the school year, and it was possible to measure the changes which had been effected in him since the earlier ordeal, both in degree and in kind. Then, he had successfully contrived a cheerful demeanour and had hidden from me any apprehension he had endured; the exams must have been for him a blind perilous leap into pitch, into a darkness which concealed a thousand traps littered over mysterious territory. Now, that territory had become more or less familiar; he knew its bounds and frontiers, had learnt the rules which governed behaviour within it, certainly enough to know which ones could be infringed with impunity, and felt reasonably sure of foot. While it would be an exaggeration to say Gary looked forward to these exams, he nevertheless approached them with something like excitement. I think he was anxious to share that tension which attends such events in a school, proud to be part of the general fevered anticipation, when every child's stomach feels like a great black hole and the upheaval in school routine and sense of impending import-ance give an extra prod to the nerve-ends, so that everyone feels like a thoroughbred about to be unleashed. Gary had had his own tensions, but they were his and his alone, not to be intruded upon, still less brought into common currency. These exam tensions were different − they enabled him to participate in a communal fear, to be one of the herd which, with one simultaneous movement of heads, apprehends the proximity of the lion and responds with a single, orchestrated, dash for cover. Gary's private despairs were of an intractable order; inarticulately, he knew he was destined forever to keep them close to him. He embraced these end-of-term tensions with something like relief, for he could feel they were the same for all the pupils, and gloried in his being part of a whole. He even, theatrically, played them up for a few days before, telling me time and again what a bag of nerves he was and looking for the ordinary reassurances which he assumed were being showered, at their various homes, upon his colleagues at school.

It was the effort he put into the written English exams which was the most astonishing. Two years earlier, he would not have deigned to touch his pencil; now, he poured forth sentences, albeit erratically spelt, to cover pages. Fortunately, the questions encouraged free expression, giving him subjects to write upon as he wished. He managed to introduce the concept of fatherhood into nearly all of them. Here is one such:

On Christmas my dad Bought me a silver tedey Bear to put on a chan. it was nice and small. I was staying at my nans house and it was stolen of my dressing tabal with my wach . . . it upseat me and my Dad was verrey angrey with me. it was the only one in England. it was bought in the USA last year by my Dad.

I do not recall this incident at all, and suspect the anecdote was an amalgam of transferred guilt (Gary was generally the perpetrator of theft, not its victim), empathy (to show that he did in fact realise what it was like to have something precious removed from one's possession), innocence (the thief is not named, suggesting it was not always possible to name him – I should take note), and pride (the relationship is real enough for Dad to be angry). If I appear to believe the answers Gary gave in his exam paper were intended really to be read by me more than the teacher, this is probably true. It is not arrogant to see one's own reflection when the image is blatant. Another question invited the pupil to talk about a book he had read. Gary chose one of mine, and finished his little essay with the remark, 'It was my Dad who roat it.'

Another strain which displayed itself was the familiarity with aggression and violence, but, here again, the point of view was not Gary's usual one. His angle of vision in his writing was contrary to that which dominated his perception of life. It is, after all, common enough for the written word to offer a release from reality, the chance to stand reality on its head, and such is the basis for the talents of many a celebrated novelist. The pen may scorn inhibition while the man remains a slave to it. I was intrigued to see how Gary had used the pen to place himself in a different relation to the world from the one which obtained in reality. There was a piece about a typical incident at a football match:

It was at Chelsea F.C. one Saterday. It was v. Mill Wall. All the Mill Wall wear up the Shed and all the Chelsea. It was a very good mach antill Mill Wall scord, then we all chased the Mill wall out of the Shed and pusht them onto the Pich. They all went up to the North Stand and then Buch Wilkins took a corner and Finaston tapt it into the goal and Mill Wall scord in the scond harf . . . we wear walking down to the station when all the Mill Wall came runing round towords us. We all teard round and run, it was like a night mear. One boy was trampled on by the Mill Wall and was heart badly. It made me feel eal to see blod all over his Face. Some men went and cauld an amblanc he was seven years old. Then I went behind a wall to see two boys beating up a Chelsea boy so I went and got the Police and thay went and arested them.

The idea of Gary assisting the police would be risible were it not for the potency of the imagined identity. Gary is not the aggressor in this story, as he was so often in life, but the saviour. I was reminded of the cryptic note he left me at the very beginning of his sojourn under my roof, in which I was depicted as the man drowning and he the rescuer bidding me to hold on tight. When he wrote, Gary was not indulging in wishful-thinking, but, more pertinently, in wish-fulfilment. In his fancies on paper, he was for once the hero, applauded by all and especially self-approved. What made the fancy significant, for me, was that it was the product of a moral being. Gary was not an amoralist, bent only on self-indulgence and indifferent to the injury he might inflict upon others; he could distinguish between right and wrong and did wrong only because, in his view, nobody would do right by him. Yet he *wanted* to do right, and in his stories he always did. He fashioned fictions wherein violence occurred and he was sickened by it; where people suffered and he came to their aid.

Two years had passed since I had sat, horrified, in the cinema while Gary bounced and beamed with untrammelled, unselfconscious joy at the wretched violence depicted on the screen. Something quite important had happened since then. He had, inwardly at least, changed sides, had learned to see that violence was not the only means of self-expression open to him and not a route which would automatically earn his respect when adopted by others. In so doing, he had taken a step which threatened to cause him untold anguish if he was ever made to recognise its import. I intuited by now that his mother had probably lived in a world soaked in the kind of violence she actively sought and needed. She had demanded that her lovers treat her with brutality, and, in a vicious spiral of frustration, had collected more and more lovers to vary and intensify the violence she enjoyed at their hands, numbing her senses with whisky the more easily to endure their blows. The infant Gary had witnessed these horrid rituals, or at least

138

some of them, and what is once in the head cannot be chucked out of it. He understood violence as the avenue down which he had to travel to earn his mother's love. If he was now, as I thought, beginning to reject violence, it could only mean that he was quietly seeing his mother in a new light. In forswearing violent behaviour, at least in intention, he would be turning his back on his mother's need, in fact rejecting her.

This was too crucial and dangerous a thought ever to articulate in Gary's presence. I did not even want him to face it. But I welcomed the development and hoped that I was right. I need hardly say, in view of all that has gone before, that my delight was premature.

The exam results were handed to Gary, as to all the pupils, in a large brown envelope, which he brought home to me. On the outside of the envelope he scrawled, in large capital letters, DO NOT HAVE A GO AT ME IF IT IS BAD. PLEASE LET ME SEE IT. GARY.

It was not bad. His marks were not high, but neither were they deplorable. He, of course, was not satisfied, for the reward was not commensurate with the massive effort he had made; were he to have been given marks which took more account of the mountain he had climbed and less of his failure to reach the summit, he would have swept the board. The task of giving due praise was one that fell to me, and I readily admit I relished it.

My pleasure was easy to delineate. It derived from the satisfaction of watching Gary progress towards some kind of maturity, and the knowledge that I had in some measure helped him along the road. My attention lay in the will to make him do well, in his own lights, and in the feeling that his struggle through the morass of confrontation, uncertainty and sheer terror which afflict the adolescent life had been guided, in however incomplete a fashion, by my experience and hindsight.

139

So often, of course, a real father grows weary of his offspring, and is too keenly aware of the conflict which has evolved in their relationship to discern the underlying need; or he has to diffuse his attentions to encompass the wants of his other children. My coming unprepared upon Gary at the very moment when the lack of guidance threatened to fragment his burgeoning personality into contorted splinters was both an advantage and a curse. I had no real knowledge of his past, nor of his still-sensitive scars, beyond what I could glean from amateur observation, and that surely inhibited my usefulness. But nor had I that backlog of irritation and over-familiarity which must sometimes stand in the way of a father faced with the rapid, bewildering changes in his adolescent son. By the time the son is most in need of his father's assistance, the filial alliance is sometimes already severed, in its deepest expression, by years of awkwardness and feuding. My pride in Gary's emergent character was a fresh plant, greenhouse-grown, not a tired and battered perennial. I was happy that he was beginning to show signs, little ones perhaps, that he would be able to act independently and responsibly.

Gary's intrusion into my life awakened values which had lain dormant for years. I had myself benefited as a child from the attentions of a teacher who had devoted much of his energies towards making sure that I would do well in those areas of life where he had failed. I must not appear to pursue the analogy too far; I do not mean to pretend that my own schooling had been as lamentable as Gary's, only that I had been destined for a banal future in factories until the teacher, with personal and, as I now see, affectionate attention, allowed me to see the horizon in another direction. The teaching had been subtle, unobtrusive, but it had remained with me throughout the subsequent years. In a way, it seemed that I had been afforded the chance to repay in kind, and that Gary was to be the ultimate beneficiary of what I had then learnt, two decades earlier. It made me recognise a salient, if platitudinous, truth — that the fruits of experience ripple onwards into the future. Gary's experience had been traumatic; mine was to temper the effects of this and smooth his passage towards adulthood. That, at any rate, was what I still hoped. I no longer thought the hope was entirely vain.

The denouement which undermined and finally crushed that hope was rapid and brutal. Events swept by, helter-skelter, forcing decisions which would have been better taken after slow reflection. Gary met a girl called Pat, like him sixteen years old, for whom he immediately conceived a consuming passion. This was not in itself unwelcome, but it became more worrying when he so ingratiated himself with Pat's parents as to offer them an entirely fictitious version of his character.

It was quite understandable that he should, and I could not reproach him for it. He wanted to create a good impression and was unlikely to do so if he were to confess to being a liar, a thief and a fantasist. Besides which, he still did not see any of these attributes as being applicable to himself as he *really* was, as he *felt* himself to be. My dilemma amounted to this: to be loyal to Gary I should let him work out his own ways towards a good relationship with this family, and not interfere with the image he skilfully, cunningly, projected. It was, after all, none of my business, and if I wanted him to grow into a mature young man who made his own progress through life, having cut loose from my 'guidance', I should leave him alone and watch how he fared. On the other hand, I knew only too well that the volatile, fragile, dangerous manifestations of Gary's personality might take these unsuspecting people by surprise. He took to staying the night occasionally at their terraced house in the East End of London, at their invitation, and they were clearly entranced by him. I felt I could not allow their house to be invaded by a concealed menace without volunteering some kind of warning. This became urgent when, after only three weeks, they tentatively suggested Gary might want to move in with them on the longer term.

As I write this now, it appears to me that I must have betrayed Gary in laying bare aspects of his behaviour which he might well have learnt to control. To him, it can only have seemed the basest treachery, although I told him frankly that I intended to have a talk with Pat's parents and that they should know more about him from me. It is not easy for me now to look upon my own conduct at this crossroads in his life with indulgence. I felt I was being responsible, but I was meddlesome and self-important, wanting my voice to be heard and my knowledge of the 'case' to be acknowledged. By a curious irony, it was Gary who reacted with what appeared to be more maturity. 'You tell them about me,' he said. 'But don't make it all black.' And there was a part of him which continued to enjoy being the subject of discussion – it was a demonstration of attention.

Pat's parents, Mr and Mrs Morris, were unsophisticated decent Cockneys, with a warm, wholesome, if somewhat cluttered family life. One daughter had married, and there was another, younger daughter still at home in addition to Pat. They shared their tiny rooms with three dogs, a canary and a cat. The kettle was perpetually on the boil for a cup of tea, the sink forever stacked with plates and cups waiting to be washed, and the pile of clothes which needed ironing never seemed to diminish. The animals scratched their fleas all day long and the ashtrays threatened to overflow, but there was a cheerfulness and ebullience about the house which was intimately endearing. I could well understand why Gary felt drawn to the Morrises; they represented that elusive normality which he had all his life been denied.

I made this very observation to Mr and Mrs Morris when I went to tea for the purpose of our discussion as to Gary's involvement with them. I told them that he would find their home ever more enticing and would want gradually to lay claim to a part of their territory. This did not worry them in the slightest degree. 'Bert never had a son,' said Mrs Morris, 'and he always wanted one. He and Gary will get on like a house on fire, you'll see. As far as we're concerned, he's welcome here any time. Ain't that right, Bert?' Mr Morris nodded his assent. He spoke little, having got used over the years to his wife speaking for both of them. 'Anyway,' she continued, 'he's good for our Pat. We'll keep an eye on them, don't you worry. They won't get up to any mischief here. Far better they stay here watching the telly and holding hands than walking the streets, that's what I say.'

I ventured to suggest that if Gary and Pat ever fell out, or their love were to turn sour, Gary would react with such mighty resentment and terror that they would find it difficult to cope. Mrs Morris was not perturbed. 'All he wants is a mother's love, poor lad,' she said. 'He won't be any problem. If he's naughty, Bert'll tell him off, won't you Bert, and he won't do it again.' Mrs Morris saw simple solutions, and her faith was enviable. 'What if he steals from you?' I asked. 'He might, you know. He may not mean to hurt you, but he can sometimes do things which are as painful as a slap in the face. He can create turmoil which appears to be a rejection of everything that you want to give him.' Mrs Morris listened with exemplary patience. 'Lordy me,' she said, 'there won't be no need for all that talk, you mark my words.'

The Morrises promised to let me know if Gary proved awkward, and on that understanding we arranged that he should stay with them at weekends. He, of course, was delighted, not only, not even principally, because he liked being there and wanted Pat's company, but because he had yet again succeeded in manipulating events to fulfil his own desires. Gary's need for omnipotence was as alive as ever.

Was there perhaps an element of jealousy in my wish to impose my advice on the Morrises? Did I obscurely feel that

143

Gary's wish to be with them smacked of desertion, or an implied reproach that the home I had provided was insufficient? I think not. On the contrary, there was a degree of very real relief that Gary would be off my hands for a couple of days a week, that I would be spared the constant threat of a rise in tension or a surprise explosion. Not only that, but I was honest enough to recognise the distinct advantages which the Morrises offered, and fully expected that, if crises could be averted, Gary would benefit magnificently by their attentions. For these reasons, I wanted him to visit them; all that I did not want was that they should be left in ignorance as to the perils inherent in what they were undertaking by opening their door to him so unselfishly.

One more proviso, which was to prove the single most calamitous mistake I made. Discipline, I imagined, was still an important ingredient in Gary's development. It must curtail his omnipotence, for his own sake, and confirm his ties to me, which I knew were still important to him. He could not disappear to the East End whenever he felt like it, but when his chores and obligations at home had first been attended to. He would go on a visit when his slate was clean, when his reward had been earned. To allow him to take off as the mood demanded would indicate that I did not particularly care whether he was at home or not, and the implied indifference would do him no good at all. The mistake was to delegate that authority to someone else in my absence.

In October I went on holiday to Ireland for two weeks. Once more, Gary was happy to be left 'in charge', with Stuart and Josie occupying the same house almost as his tenants. He undertook not to go to see Pat until Saturday, and not then until he had cleaned and tidied his room and done some shopping for Mrs Hardcastle. He would naturally go to school as usual. Stuart was aware of these stipulations. I took a flight to Belfast confident that the household would continue happily; I was even a little radiant that such progress had been

144

made that it was possible to trust Gary with a considerable amount of responsibility for himself.

Shortly after my arrival in County Donegal there came a telephone call from Stuart in London. I knew immediately that the occasion for such a call must be grave, because it was extremely difficult to make any telephone contact with that remote part of Ireland, and Stuart would not submit himself to the ordeal of trying for two hours or more unless the effort were truly warranted.

I could barely hear his voice through the crackle and grit on the line – he might have been in Tierra del Fuego. 'I've got bad news for you,' he said.

'What is it?'

'Gary's been stealing again.'

'What, from you?'

'No, that wouldn't bother me so much. It's the shop on the corner, Turner's. He was caught with his hand in the till while the cashier was helping a mate of his, obviously a set-up job. One takes her attention while the other takes the loot. Apparently it's not the first time. He says he's been using the money to buy a ring for his girlfriend, as if that makes it all right.'

'Has he bought the ring?'

'Yes, he showed it to me, all proud.'

'Who knows about this, apart from you?'

'I'm afraid nearly everyone. The shop-girl called the police, and they have been here to see Gary. They know about you, and asked where you were, implying that you should have been here. Foster-fathers don't go on holiday, they said. I did my best to placate them, but Gary didn't help. He was belligerent and surly. They wanted you to come back straight away, but I said travel from there wasn't easy, so they have left it on the back burner till you get back. But Gary is going to be watched whenever he goes out of the house. I've got a feeling the blokes on the beat have been told to keep their eye on him.'

145

'What does Gary say to all this?'

'He doesn't much. He won't talk to me, except to throw his weight around and pretend he doesn't care. I'm not sure he does. There's no sign of guilt, remorse or regret.'

To my despondency and horror, I realised in a flash that, after all this time, I was still not surprised by Gary's moral disfigurement, which burgeoned forth regularly like a crippled and stained bloom from an apparently robust plant.

'Shall I get him on the line?' asked Stuart.

'No, better not,' I said. 'Let him wonder.'

Perhaps I should have faced him, or made him face me, on the telephone. I have often wondered since. He needed to feel that I was sufficiently angry not to want to talk to him, but he also needed to feel that, whatever his crimes, he was safe from loveless retribution visited from without the family unit, such as it was. How to balance these two opposing imperatives had ever been the blot of indecision on my programme. I think now I lost control of the balance and allowed that precious equilibrium to topple.

Pompously, I thought it my duty to inform the Morrises in East London and wrote Mr Morris a letter suggesting that he might like to confiscate the ring until Gary had earned the money to pay for it. In fact, I wanted an ally, or someone to share the blame if blame there should later be, and hijacked Mr Morris into that role. Gary had found the Morrises through their daughter Pat, had charmed and beguiled them, saw a promise of happiness with them, and here was I now stealing the Morrises' goodwill for myself. One theft deserved another.

I do not say that this attitude was consciously adopted, but its repercussions were serious whatever its source. About four days later there was another strangled call from London. This time it was Josie. She was sobbing. Gary had attacked Stuart while she was out. I resolved to leave Donegal there and then, took a fast car to Belfast and waited for the first spare seat on a shuttle. When I turned up in London, Gary was in his room, sitting on the floor in a corner. I had never seen him do this before. He looked at me with eyes which mingled hatred, fear, hurt. He was like a cornered animal. 'You don't need to ask me anything,' he said, 'so don't waste your breath. *They'll* tell you anything you want to know.'

Not having been present, I cannot describe exactly what had occurred, and indeed Gary chided me more than once for believing the account of 'the enemy' too readily. I suppose he knew I was less likely to believe any re-ordered account he might give, and, by that admission of bias alone, revealed myself to have been, all along, part of the hostile forces ranged against him. Friendship, love, alliance, were to Gary synonymous with the rejection of all opinion or fact which might threaten to be hostile, the abandonment of all pretence at fair play, the denial of objectivity. One had to be loyal or one was nothing. The grandmother was loyal. She knew the rules. And who is to say they were not right, the pair of them? How common it is to see the families of the most gruesome criminals burst into loud lamentation and promise of revenge when their 'innocent' member is found guilty in the dock. They *know* he is a murderer, or a terrorist, or a crook, and that, objectively speaking, he did what he has been accused of doing. But there is no place for objectivity in the fierce togetherness of family. Those tears from the public gallery are not shed for the shame of seeing injustice done, but to cement the bonds, to share the pain and humiliation, even to take some of the guilt into one's heart. It is a bonding which ascends beyond the faint-hearted moralities of civilised life to the tribal exigencies of the ancestral pack-animal. Truth and decency are but feeble abstractions which can do little against such primitive power.

I listened head in hands to Stuart's grim and full account of what had happened. Gary had apparently been truanting both before and after he had stolen the money to buy Pat's ring. One day he said he didn't feel well and was going to stay in bed instead of going to school. Stuart said all right, but that he must genuinely stay in his bed. Gary later got up, dressed, and made to leave the house. I don't know if Stuart actually barred his way, but he certainly attempted to act as my proxy, to do or say what I would have done or said had I been there, and thereby assume an authority which was not strictly his. Although Stuart, in so doing, acted in Gary's interest, or so he thought, what he achieved was to fracture, in a few crucial seconds, that fragile manufactured connection between the boy and the only restraint on his actions he was prepared to recognise, vested in me.

Gary's eyes went cold. His pupils shrank to menacing pinheads. Slowly and deliberately, he turned his back and went to the kitchen. When he faced Stuart once more, he held aloft a long, threatening carving-knife. There was no doubt in Stuart's mind that he intended to use it. A fight ensued, furniture was hurled over, Stuart managing to grab Gary by the wrists and hold him at bay, while he, Gary, began to salivate wildly. He swung free and ran out into the hall, then returned and locked the door to the kitchen, imprisoning Stuart. The doorbell rang. It was a colleague of Stuart's from the BBC. Gary would not answer it, and Stuart could not. The man, hearing unnaturally shrill shouting from inside, went to the neighbour next door, climbed over the dividing wall, and entered the house through the back door. Together, he and Stuart forced the kitchen door and disarmed Gary, who turned, ran upstairs, and slammed the door behind him, unapproachable in the security of his room.

Stuart collapsed from the effort, sweat moistening his forehead and lip as he took stock of the disaster only narrowly averted. Later, he went up to confront Gary in a spirit of friendly reconciliation, but the chastened boy would not answer the knocks on his door. It was then that Josie had come in and telephoned me in Ireland.

From Stuart's point of view, the blame was entirely mine, and he may well have been right. I ought not to have simply decamped and left him to deal with an impossible situation. It was maniacally irresponsible of me. Stuart had nearly been killed, and indeed it was pure luck that I did not return to a blood-spattered house, a corpse, and a sackful of difficult questions. Gary had been transfigured by fierce blind hatred and could no longer manage his own responses or behaviour. To this day, Stuart has never entirely forgiven my selfishness.

I told Gary that there was no possibility of his staying in the house for the moment — he would have to go to his grand-mother while I thought things through. He left resignedly, sadly, as one who has been robbed of his few belongings and cannot summon the heart to begin all over again. There were no bitter recriminations, just a muttered phrase: 'You shouldn't've let him try to tell me what to do. It's my house.'

From Nan's flat he wrote me a note, which I received the next day:

Dear Brian, I am sorry that I spoilt your holiday as you gave such a good holiday in France and it was verry kind of you and you must know I am verry gratfull to you. But you shood of not toled pat's dad that I took that money from the shop and that Pat shood sell the ring because it means a lot to her and me but I will pay you back the money. But pleas let pat keep the ring. I have had a fue afternoons of to look for a job but i have not much success but dont be angrey with me but i can not blam you if you are. I did try my hardist to stay at school but i was dertermind to get a job but i could not but i did try my hardist.

YOUR LOVING SON
Gary Masters

A parent, I thought, never turfs his child out of the house, no matter what the fault. I had demolished the very structure

I had striven to build. From that moment it was understood that Gary would beat a new path. This one had not worked.

As Gary took more and more to staying at his new East End retreat for several days at a time (having returned to me from his grandmother's after a week), it became clear that he was inching towards departure. His battle with Stuart had confirmed his bleak black view that the world rested on power and that whoever exercised it would be King. He felt deposed, and needed to seek out a new kingdom. Mercifully, he did not feel so undermined that he simply got up and went. He retained a residue of acknowledgment that my own 'power' to influence his fate was still something he wanted to preserve, so that he would not leave for a new life without my permission and blessing. Every other opinion, he knew, would be against his moving. But mine was the only one he would take account of.

Gary had one term left to complete at school. For that reason alone, it would be foolish for him to launch into new surroundings with a new set of threatening competitors for just three months, a prospect which would normally have set him jumping with ill-disguised fear. Even this anxiety was overcome, however, by his all-conquering need to be close to Pat. He sent her notes constantly. One which he left behind, probably because he wanted to re-fashion it in more lordly style, said this:

Dear Pat, I do love you and hope you love me too but I shall always love you. yes I will. I mean it because it is true. *If you do not want to go out with me pleas tell me.*

His curious use of the conjunction 'but', in this letter as in many others, seemed to indicate a permanent anticipation of opposition, as if everything he wanted to say would be met by denial or prevention, and the 'but' was always prematurely at the ready to deal with these hurdles. No letters from Pat ever arrived at the house, so I presumed she was not the epistolary sort. I hoped it did not presage lukewarm affections on her part.

There was a much more crucial reason why he should not move. I felt that he should learn to cope with setbacks and disappointments and should not seek with alacrity a fresh 'magic wand' to sweep aside the difficulties that befell him. He would sooner or later have to understand the real world if he was to find a place within it, not avoid it by escape into a different world of his own devising. I told him as much. He understood, but did not want to accept.

Arrangements were made for him to be interviewed by the headmaster of a school in the East End. Gary was more nervous at this encounter than I had ever seen him before, and after it, collapsed into uncontrollable sobs. His very survival seemed to depend on his being able to prove himself worthy, and the head was so searching in his questions, so strictly factual and unbending, that the absence of compassion left Gary feeling, for the first time, unspecial. The experience entirely scissored him.

I was anxious that a 'case conference' be convened as soon as possible, with all the people who had played a part in Gary's development over the past two and a half years to be summoned. Most of them were reluctant, with good reason. It was Mrs Branfield, the paediatric psychiatrist, who voiced their doubts most effectively. I had carefully and purposefully avoided prying into Gary's relationship with Mrs Branfield, on the reasonable grounds that it should be a corner of his life over which I had no influence and would venture no opinion. I did not even know if he kept his appointments. Only now did I discover that he had been unusually reliable and had missed few consultations. He had been free to talk about whatever he liked, or to shut up and remain in sullen silence if

151

he preferred, and as a result had come closer into touch with his own weaknesses. Mrs Branfield never revealed the substance of their chats, but she led me to believe that a lot of time was spent chewing over my behaviour, achievements, expectations, faults, as Gary grappled with the new game of analysis; having worked me out, he was turning the searchlight upon himself. This had at one session caused tears of frustration with his own intractable soul. Now Mrs Branfield advised against 'rushing into' anything. She wrote:

> While I think it is important for everyone concerned to meet to discuss the situation, I think the very urgency that is about at the moment can tell us something of the way in which Gary affects all those people around him to take action on his behalf. I therefore think that this is a crucial time for Gary to work out what his relationship with you means to him, rather than to move on to another set of relationships, leaving unfinished business behind . . . I do realise that the events of the last few weeks must have been very disturbing for you, and I do hope that it will be possible for you and Gary to reflect on what has happened rather than to make immediate arrangements for his transfer elsewhere.

In other words, Gary was once again manipulating, and should be stopped. Still, I found myself thinking, should he be stopped merely because adults resented being manipulated by a boy of his age? If manipulation was his lever on the world, on *his* world, should it necessarily be wrenched from his hand, leaving him defenceless, emasculated, shipwrecked? The manipulative art was his one greatest talent. To deprive him of this, by a conspiracy of wisdom, would be to rob him of faith in himself, to denude him, to conquer his will and flail his spirit. There was something selfishly cruel in this, especially when one considered the number of adult, sophisticated people scattered through life who make a virtue of manipulation, from politicians to advertisers to newspaper editors, without being condemned for it. I felt progressively drawn to Gary's side, all the while bearing in mind that I might be easily persuaded through an unspoken desire on my part to be rid of a troublesome problem.

I was still undecided, but it was Gary who stated the position with utmost clarity, unexpectedly, steering me towards certainty. We did sit down and have the discussion which the psychiatrist recommended, though it was not along the lines she had envisaged. For once, Gary did not wait for me to initiate and winkle out responses from him; it was he who opened the conversation, followed it through with calm reason devoid of hostility or fear, and carried me to a conclusion. He had never before been so sensible, honest, or self-examining, and I admit I was moved by the change in him.

'I've never known what it's like to live with a mother and father,' he said. 'It might have happened once, for a month or two, but I was too young ever to know about it. I have had to watch other kids take it all for granted, having parents at home and all that, and don't think I haven't noticed. I can't say I missed it, 'cause I never knew it, but I sure as Hell saw it, and always wondered what it would be like. Perhaps I'd be a different bloke now if I'd had parents, just like that, always there and always at home. Kids don't know how lucky they are, they really don't. It's all in a day's work for them, normal like, they don't even have to think about it. I've been thinking about it all my life, and always wondered if I would ever get to know what it's like. I know you've tried to be Mum and Dad to me, I've watched you trying, and I wanted you to try too, 'cause I thought well, at least one parent's better than none, innit? But you can't. You can't be Mum and Dad, no one can. There's got to be two of you, so I can feel I'm half of each. Otherwise it's something different. Look, I'm getting older all

153

the time. This may be my last chance, my last chance *ever*, to know what it's like. Pat's mum and dad want to be my mum and dad. I dunno why, but they do. It's now or never, Brian. If you don't let me go, I'll never have another chance. I just want to see what it's like, just for once. They won't do it unless you say yes. Will you?'

In the face of such artless eloquence, I capitulated. I could not deny him one more new experience before, as he said, he altogether ceased to be a child. The relevant authorities were informed of the *fait accompli*, Gary stripped pictures from his walls, emptied drawers, smothered the dog with kisses every five minutes, packed his bags gleefully, and left, sitting next to me in the car with a grin from ear to ear. Gone were the erstwhile accompaniments to excitement, the thumping of fist on doors, the shrieking and explosive release of energy. He was quietly happy. There was no sadness or glumness – I was glad of that. Gary had grown up.

Two days later there came one of his ingenuous letters. 'Thank you for macking it so I can come down to Hackney,' he wrote. 'I will always be grateful to you for every think you have done over the last fue years and for being such a good father to me. I do not forget you and I will always be in tuch with you. I have seteld in and will see you soon. Your son, Gary.'

EPILOGUE

IT WAS FOOLISH for me to imagine I could do any lasting good. Gary's star had been thwarted and knocked askew by unfair inheritance and a disastrous early life. The adult he would become had been determined in those first few years by this awesome combination, and no subsequent influence could alter his fundamental direction. He had been robbed of the basic freedom to choose himself.

Naturally, I did not realise this when he first came in search of conquest, claiming for himself a tiny portion of that happiness which he sensed was everywhere around him but never in him, and which, with bitter resignation, he had assumed was not his to share. Yet, having realised it, I would still maintain it was worth trying. Resignation is death to the soul, an emotional and spiritual road-block, with which no child should be burdened. Any attempt to shift the blockage, even if foredoomed, is better than weak woeful abnegation. Albert Camus devoted his intellectual vigour to the notion that the effort was all, and he was right.

The wretched irony is that it was I who gained most from the experience of looking after Gary. In so far as the object was for him to learn to be at ease with himself, to respect and love himself rather than to revere the power-maniac of his imagination, there were fitful signs of success. But he never learnt fully to understand his own personality, still less to deploy

155

any such knowledge in his dealings with others, whereas I daily gathered to me fresh insights into the intricate puzzle of human behaviour, and learnt, sometimes at least, to see what lay behind it as well as to grasp and delay it. So, I was the beneficiary. I had sought to be of use to Gary, and I had used him.

There was a negative benefit, too. I resolved never again to allow myself to be hoodwinked by charm, always to nurture detachment, always to retreat from dependent closeness with other humans. I did not want to be battered again. Of course, I have not succeeded, because the will is notoriously inefficient in this area, but the very fact that I designed such a change in my values is witness to Gary's influence upon *me*. He made me see the world through his eyes, not with reason and argument but by affective identification, and what I saw troubled me to such an extent that I began to feel, and still do feel, that human relationships are inherently dangerous. This is the very opposite of what I had intended. Gary's legacy with me is palpable; mine with him probably evanescent.

I have no way of knowing what is in his mind now. He stayed with his new family in the East End for little more than a year, and never did complete his schooling. His love for Pat diminished, for reasons presumably unknown even to him, he took a job with a local garage for about a month, and eventually returned to the all-forgiving breast of his grandmother. She died shortly afterwards, leaving him a small fortune in five-pound notes. He spent all this in months. Pat died of a rare disease at the age of nineteen. Gary married, fathered two children, divorced and returned to his wife, all before he was twenty-three. He called in to see me, always unannounced, about once every three years, buoyant with boasts and bravado. He was habitually reticent about his address, and I formed the impression he would stay with whoever would have him for a few weeks, be it ex-wife or new mistress, then disappear anew.

156

One thought recurs every now and then. Gary has again separated from his wife, and the children live with their mother. His devotion to them is characteristically fierce; he has told me he would die for them, and I believe him. It is a cruel reflection, but it would be tragic if the children were to ingest the distorted moral outlook, the impotent fury which it appears their father may still carry with him. He seems to live in a condition of permanent anger, for which an object must repeatedly be found. I would not want to think the damage he endured he is bound to pass on, like a vicious booby-trapped heirloom, repeating the cycle for who knows how many generations. The son is father to the man. No one can supplant him.